Financial Statements of Limited Companies

Workbook

David Cox

Published by Osborne Books Limited
Tel 01905 748071
Email books@osbornebooks.co.uk
Website www.osbornebooks.co.uk

Design by Laura Ingham

Printed by CPI Group (UK) Limited, Croydon, CR0 4YY, on environmentally friendly, acid-free paper from managed forests.

MIX
Paper from
responsible sources
FSC® C019777

British Library Cataloguing in Publication Data
A catalogue record for this book is available from the British Library

ISBN 978 1909173 866

Contents

Introduction

Qualifications covered

This book has been written specifically to cover the Unit 'Financial Statements of Limited Companies' which is mandatory for the following qualifications:

AAT Professional Diploma in Accounting – Level 4

AAT Professional Diploma in Accounting at SCQF – Level 8

This book contains Chapter Activities which provide extra practice material in addition to the activities included in the Osborne Books Tutorial text, and Practice Assessments to prepare the student for the computer based assessments. The latter are based directly on the structure, style and content of the sample assessment material provided by the AAT at www.aat.org.uk.

Suggested answers to the Chapter Activities and Practice Assessments are set out in this book.

Osborne Study and Revision Materials

The materials featured on the previous page are tailored to the needs of students studying this Unit and revising for the assessment. They include:

- **Tutorials:** paperback books with practice activities
- **Student Zone:** access to Osborne Books online resources
- **Osborne Books App:** Osborne Books ebooks for mobiles and tablets

Visit www.osbornebooks.co.uk for details of study and revision resources and access to online material.

Chapter activities

1 Purpose of financial statements

1.1 **(a)** What is the objective of financial statements according to the *Conceptual Framework for Financial Reporting*?

(b) For the three user groups identified in the *Conceptual Framework for Financial Reporting*, identify their purposes in using financial reporting information.

1.2 Which **one** of the following statements is correct?

(a) income – expenses = profits or losses	
(b) assets – expenses = profits or losses	
(c) assets + expenses = profits or losses	
(d) income + expenses = profits or losses	

1.3 Which **one** of the following options is correct?

	Assets £	Equity £	Liabilities £	
(a)	20,600	28,950	8,350	
(b)	16,850	7,900	7,950	
(c)	18,550	10,530	8,200	
(d)	35,250	20,650	14,600	

1.4 The *Conceptual Framework for Financial Reporting* identifies four enhancing qualitative characteristics that make the information provided in financial statements useful to users.

Write in the enhancing qualitative characteristic that relates to each of the statements below.

Statement	Characteristic
Financial information that is available to decision-makers in time to be capable in influencing their decisions	
Financial information that helps assure users that information is faithfully represented	
Users of financial statements are able to identify and understand similarities in, and differences among, items	
Users of financial statements are presented with information that is classified and characterised clearly and concisely	

1.5 **(a)** Set out the accounting equation and define the elements in the equation.

(b) Briefly explain how profit for the year affects the elements of the accounting equation.

1.6 **(a)** What are the elements that appear in financial statements according to the *Conceptual Framework for Financial Reporting*?

(b) Define the elements that appear in the statement of profit or loss and other comprehensive income in accordance with the definitions in the *Conceptual Framework for Financial Reporting*.

1.7   You are the accountant preparing the financial statements of Faye Ltd for the financial year just ended. The directors wish to show the lowest possible profit for the year in order to pay less corporation tax. To achieve this they are pressuring you to report a reduced and incorrect figure for revenue.

Identify and explain the relevant fundamental principle in accordance with AAT's Code of Professional Ethics.

1.8   You are the accountant preparing the financial statements of Rayner Ltd for the financial year just ended. A friend of yours works for Rayner Ltd and you know that she receives an annual bonus based on the profits of the company. At a social event your friend asks, "How are the profits looking for the year? I am hoping for a good bonus this year."

Identify and explain the relevant fundamental principle in accordance with AAT's Code of Professional Ethics.

1.9   A friend of yours is currently studying units of the AAT Professional Diploma in Accounting – Level 4. A few days ago you saw an advertisement in the local newspaper where your friend offers a full range of professional accountancy services, stating that she has many years of experience, and has a large number of satisfied clients.

Identify and explain the relevant fundamental principle in accordance with AAT's Code of Professional Ethics.

1.10   For each of the following statements identify the relevant fundamental principle in accordance with AAT's Code of Professional Ethics.

Statement	Fundamental principle
The manager of an accountancy firm arranges appropriate training and supervision for staff	
An accountant suggests to a prospective client that the client's current accountants are providing a poor service	
An accounting report contains a misleading statement	
An accountant must avoid situations that unduly influence professional judgement	
An accountant discusses the financial results of a client's business with friends	

1.11   **(a)**   According to the IASB's *Conceptual Framework for Financial Reporting,* what are the two fundamental qualitative characteristics that make financial information useful?

(b)   Explain what is meant by each of the two fundamental qualitative characteristics.

2 Introduction to limited company financial statements

- Blank photocopiable pro-formas in the format used in AAT Assessments – of the statement of profit or loss and other comprehensive income and the statement of financial position, are included in the Appendix – it is advisable to enlarge them to full A4 size. Blank workings sheets are also included in the Appendix.

- Pro-formas and workings sheets are also available to download from www.osbornebooks.co.uk.

2.1 **(a)** Define a public limited company (plc)

(b) Define a private limited company (ltd)

2.2 What is meant by a limited company having a separate legal entity? Select **one** of the following:

(a) The name of the company is different from that of the individual shareholders	
(b) Anyone taking legal action proceeds against the company and not the individual shareholders	
(c) The company must submit financial statements to Companies House	
(d) The directors manage the company on behalf of shareholders	

2.3 Which one of the following investments in a company usually carries voting rights at meetings of the company?

(a) Ordinary shares	
(b) Preference shares	
(c) Debentures	
(d) Long-term loans	

2.4   A new company issues 100,000 ordinary shares of 50p each at a premium of 10 per cent. What amount will be shown as the total of the equity section of the company's statement of financial position?

(a) £100,000	
(b) £110,000	
(c) £50,000	
(d) £55,000	

2.5   Crantock Ltd prepares its financial statements to 31 March each year. At 31 March 20-2 its trial balance was as follows:

	£000	£000
Administrative expenses	240	
Share capital		700
Trade and other receivables	525	
Cash and cash equivalents	75	
Share premium		200
Distribution costs	500	
Plant and equipment at cost	1,600	
Accumulated depreciation on plant and equipment		500
Retained earnings at 1 April 20-1		350
Purchases	1,200	
Inventories at 1 April 20-1	160	
Trade and other payables		395
Sales revenue		2,295
Dividends paid	140	
	4,440	4,440

Further information:

- Inventories at 31 March 20-2 cost £180,000.
- The corporation tax charge for the year has been calculated as £65,000.
- Depreciation on plant and equipment has already been provided for in the list of balances above and allocated to distribution costs and administrative expenses accordingly.

Required:

Prepare the financial statements of Crantock Ltd for the year ended 31 March 20-2.

2.6 Playfair Ltd prepares its financial statements to 31 December each year. At 31 December 20-3 its trial balance was as follows:

	£000	£000
Share capital		380
Share premium		50
Plant and equipment at cost	800	
Trade receivables	350	
Trade payables		160
Accruals		30
Prepayments	40	
Cash and cash equivalents	140	
Loan (non-current)		200
Inventories at 1 January 20-3	250	
Administrative expenses	110	
Purchases	1,650	
Sales revenue		2,340
Loan interest paid	40	
Distribution costs	240	
Accumulated depreciation on plant and equipment		230
Dividends paid	50	
Retained earnings at 1 January 20-3		260
Allowance for doubtful debts at 1 January 20-3		20
	3,670	3,670

Further information:

- Inventories at 31 December 20-3 cost £280,000.

- Depreciation of plant and equipment is to be charged at the rate of 20 per cent per annum on cost and allocated equally between distribution costs and administrative expenses.

- The allowance for doubtful debts is to be increased to £40,000.

- The corporation tax charge for the year has been calculated as £30,000.

Required:

Prepare the financial statements of Playfair Ltd for the year to 31 December 20-3.

3   Published financial statements of limited companies

- Blank photocopiable pro-formas in the format used in AAT Assessments – of the statement of profit or loss and other comprehensive income, the statement of changes in equity, and the statement of financial position, are included in the Appendix – it is advisable to enlarge them to full A4 size. Blank workings sheets are also included in the Appendix.

- Pro-formas and workings sheets are also available to download from www.osbornebooks.co.uk.

3.1   Complete the following sentence taken from IAS 1, *Presentation of Financial Statements*:

'The objective of financial statements is to provide [   ] about the [   ] position, financial [   ] and [   ] flows of an entity that is [   ] to a wide range of [   ] in making [   ] decisions.'

Choose from the following words:

cash

economic

financial

information

performance

useful

users

3.2   Under IAS 1, *Presentation of Financial Statements*, which of the following is included in a complete set of financial statements?

1   Statement of profit or loss and other comprehensive income
2   Statement of cash flows
3   Directors' report
4   Statement of changes in equity

(a) 1 and 2	
(b) 1, 2 and 3	
(c) 1, 2 and 4	
(d) all of them	

3.3   What are the deadlines for filing the statutory accounts with the Registrar of Companies for (1) a private limited company and (2) a public limited company?

(a) (1) nine months	(2) nine months
(b) (1) six months	(2) six months
(c) (1) six months	(2) nine months
(d) (1) nine months	(2) six months

3.4   Which of the following is included under the heading for 'Equity' in a statement of financial position?

1   Revaluation surplus
2   Bank loans
3   Share premium
4   Long-term provisions

(a)   1 and 2
(b)   1, 2 and 3
(c)   1 and 3
(d)   all of them

3.5   Which of the following involves a cash flow?

1   A rights issue of shares
2   The revaluation of a non-current asset
3   Depreciation of non-current assets
4   A bonus issue of shares

(a)   1
(b)   1 and 2
(c)   1, 2 and 3
(d)   all of them

3.6   You have been asked to help prepare the financial statements of Wymark Ltd for the year ended 31 March 20-4. The company's trial balance as at 31 March 20-4 and further information is shown below.

Wymark Ltd

Trial balance as at 31 March 20-4

	Debit	Credit
	£000	£000
Share capital		3,500
Prepayments	42	
Trade and other payables		1,309
Land and buildings – value/cost	5,000	
– accumulated depreciation at 1 April 20-3		702
Plant and equipment – cost	2,722	
– accumulated depreciation at 1 April 20-3		1,402
Trade and other receivables	1,802	
Accruals		105
8% bank loan repayable 20-9		2,500
Cash and cash equivalents	155	
Retained earnings at 1 April 20-3		1,457
Interest paid	200	
Sales revenue		10,884
Purchases	7,854	
Distribution costs	980	
Administrative expenses	461	
Inventories at 1 April 20-3	2,043	
Dividends paid	600	
	21,859	21,859

Further information:

- The inventories at the close of business on 31 March 20-4 cost £2,422,000.

- Land, which is not depreciated, is included in the trial balance at a value of £3,500,000. It is to be revalued at £4,000,000 and this revaluation is to be included in the financial statements for the year ended 31 March 20-4.

- Depreciation is to be provided for the year to 31 March 20-4 as follows:

    Buildings   2% per annum   Straight-line basis

    Plant and equipment   25% per annum   Reducing (diminishing) balance basis

• Depreciation is to be apportioned as follows:

	%
Cost of sales	50
Distribution costs	30
Administrative expenses	20

• Trade receivables include a debt of £11,000 which is to be written off. Bad (irrecoverable) debts are to be classified as administrative expenses.

• Distribution costs of £12,000 owing at 31 March 20-4 are to be provided for.

• The corporation tax charge for the year has been calculated as £348,000.

• All of the operations are continuing operations.

Required:

(a) Draft the statement of profit or loss and other comprehensive income for Wymark Ltd for the year ended 31 March 20-4.

(b) Draft the statement of changes in equity for Wymark Ltd for the year ended 31 March 20-4.

(c) Draft the statement of financial position for Wymark Ltd as at 31 March 20-4.

3.7 You have been asked to help prepare the financial statements of Nathan Ltd for the year ended 31 March 20-1. The company's trial balance as at 31 March 20-1 and further information is shown below.

Nathan Ltd

Trial balance as at 31 March 20-1

	Debit	Credit
	£000	£000
Share capital		6,000
Share premium		1,000
Trade and other payables		1,010
Prepayments	186	
Returns outwards		47
Plant and equipment – cost	20,500	
– accumulated depreciation at 1 April 20-0		4,600
Trade and other receivables	1,546	
Accruals		85
5% bank loan repayable 20-8		3,000
Cash and cash equivalents	110	
Retained earnings at 1 April 20-0		2,537
Interest paid	150	
Sales revenue		21,495
Purchases	9,364	
Distribution costs	3,852	
Administrative expenses	2,975	
Inventories at 1 April 20-0	641	
Dividends paid	450	
	39,774	39,774

Further information:

- The inventories at the close of business on 31 March 20-1 cost £627,000.
- Depreciation is to be provided on plant and equipment for the year to 31 March 20-1 at 25% per annum using the reducing (diminishing) balance basis. Depreciation is to be apportioned 60% to distribution costs and 40% to administrative expenses.
- Trade receivables include a debt of £12,000 which is to be written off. Bad (irrecoverable) debts are to be classified as administrative expenses.
- Distribution costs of £22,000 owing at 31 March 20-1 are to be provided for.
- The corporation tax charge for the year has been calculated as £207,000.
- All of the operations are continuing operations.

Required:

(a) Draft the statement of profit or loss and other comprehensive income for Nathan Ltd for the year ended 31 March 20-1.

(b) Draft the statement of changes in equity for Nathan Ltd for the year ended 31 March 20-1.

(c) Draft the statement of financial position for Nathan Ltd as at 31 March 20-1.

4 Accounting for assets

4.1 **Task 1**

What are the two criteria stated by IAS 16, *Property, Plant and Equipment*, for an item of PPE to be recognised as an asset?

Task 2

IAS 16 states that, initially, PPE are measured at cost on the statement of financial position.

(a) Explain what is meant by 'cost'.

(b) State two attributable costs which **can be included** in the cost of an asset.

(c) State two costs which **cannot be included** in the cost of an asset.

(d) Briefly explain the two models from which an entity must choose as its accounting policy after acquisition of PPE.

4.2 With reference to IAS 16, *Property, Plant and Equipment*, you are to:

(a) Define depreciation.

(b) Summarise the points a company must consider when accounting for IAS 16.

4.3 According to IAS 38, *Intangible Assets*, which **one** of the following is not a criteria for capitalising development costs by a business entity?

(a) The entity intends to complete the intangible asset and to use or sell it	
(b) The entity has no specific aim or application for the intangible asset	
(c) The entity has the resources available to complete the development and to use or sell the intangible asset	
(d) The entity has the ability to measure the development expenditure reliably	

4.4 IAS 38, *Intangible Assets*, gives three key elements of an intangible asset. Which **one** of the following is **not** one of the three key elements?

(a) Reliability	
(b) Identifiability	
(c) Control	
(d) Future economic benefits	

4.5 The directors of Tanhosier Ltd are about to undertake the development of a new product. They expect the costs of development to be significant and are concerned at the impact that this might have on their financial statements.

You have been asked to prepare notes to deal with the following queries of the directors:

(a) What is an intangible asset?

(b) What would have to be demonstrated by Tanhosier Ltd before an intangible asset arising from development is recognised as an intangible asset in the financial statements?

4.6 To which of the following assets does IAS 36, *Impairment of Assets*, apply?

1   Land and buildings
2   Inventories
3   Goodwill
4   Vehicles

(a) all of them	
(b) 1 and 2	
(c) 1, 2 and 3	
(d) 1, 3 and 4	

4.7   **Task 1**

Identify **two** external and **two** internal indicators of impairment.

Task 2

(a)   Explain what is meant by an impairment review.

(b)   How is an impairment review carried out?

4.8   A business has four assets which the directors wish to test for impairment:

Asset	Carrying amount	Fair value, less costs of disposal	Value in use
	£	£	£
1	12,000	11,000	10,000
2	8,000	8,000	9,000
3	15,000	12,000	14,000
4	17,000	19,000	18,000

Which of the above assets is impaired according to IAS 36, *Impairment of Assets*?

(a) 1	
(b) 2	
(c) 1 and 3	
(d) 2 and 4	

4.9   The directors of Burton Ltd are concerned that one of the company's items of plant and machinery might have become impaired.

The following information applies:

Carrying amount	£44,000
Fair value	£43,500
Costs of disposal	£1,200
Value in use	£40,500

What is the amount of the impairment loss that will be recognised in the statement of profit or loss, in accordance with IAS 36, *Impairment of Assets*?

(a) £NIL	
(b) £1,700	
(c) £1,800	
(d) £3,500	

4.10 The directors of Wardle Ltd are preparing the company's annual financial statements and are considering the requirements of IAS 36, *Impairment of Assets*. They understand that they will need to determine the recoverable amount of an asset and calculate whether the asset has suffered an impairment loss, when there is some indication that the asset might be impaired.

The following information relates to an item of plant and machinery owned by Wardle Ltd at its accounting year-end:

Original cost	£220,000
Accumulated depreciation	£95,000
Fair value	£120,000
Costs of disposal	£3,000
Value in use	£122,000

Answer the following:

(a) Explain how the directors of Wardle Ltd should determine the recoverable amount of an asset, illustrating your answer with reference to the item of plant and machinery owned at the company's year-end.

(b) Explain how the directors of Wardle Ltd should calculate whether an asset has suffered an impairment loss, again illustrating your answer with reference to the item of plant and machinery owned at the year-end.

4.11 Interest of £4,500 on a finance lease is to be apportioned over the lease term of five years from 20-1 to 20-5. State the finance charge amounts that will be debited to each year's statement of profit or loss and other comprehensive income using the-sum-of-the-digits method.

Year	Finance charge £
20-1	
20-2	
20-3	
20-4	
20-5	

4.12 Wentworth Ltd is about to enter into two leases for items of equipment. The terms of the first lease require the company to make lease payments of £9,000 per annum with a lease term of four years. The present value of the minimum lease payments is £28,000, the fair value of the equipment is £30,000 and its economic life is five years. The second lease is for a term of two years and Wentworth Ltd is required to make lease payments of £300 per month. The fair value of this item of equipment is £12,000 and its economic life is seven years.

The directors of Wentworth Ltd understand that the accounting treatment of each lease will depend upon whether it is to be classified as a finance lease or as an operating lease, but are unsure as to the requirements of IAS 17, *Leases*, both in terms of when a lease should be classified as a finance lease or as an operating lease, and how the two types of lease should be accounted for.

Prepare brief notes for the directors of Wentworth Ltd to cover the following:

(a) When should a lease be classified as a finance lease and when should it be classified as an operating lease according to IAS 17, *Leases*?

(b) **(1)** Explain how a finance lease is accounted for in the financial statements of the lessee at the commencement of the lease term only.

(2) Explain how an operating lease is accounted for in the financial statements of the lessee.

(c) Which of the two leases Wentworth Ltd is about to enter into, if any, would be classified as a finance lease

4.13 **(a)** Explain the two inventory valuation methods allowed by IAS 2, *Inventories*.

(b) Which method of inventory valuation cannot be used under IAS 2?

4.14 Which one of the following statements best describes the valuation of inventories under IAS 2, *Inventories* at the end of the financial year?

(a) At the lower of FIFO and AVCO	
(b) At the lower of cost and net realisable value	
(c) At the higher of FIFO and AVCO	
(d) At the higher of cost and net realisable value	

4.15 You have been asked to assist the directors of Lawnderer Limited, a company that markets and distributes lawnmowers and other garden machinery, in the preparation of the financial statements for the year ended 30 September 20-5.

The directors of the company have had a meeting with you regarding the possible treatment of certain future expenditure in the financial statements of the company. They have told you that the company has been approached by an inventor who has an idea to develop a revolutionary new lawnmower. The project looks technically feasible and preliminary marketing studies suggest a significant market for that product. Cost and revenue projections suggest that future profits should adequately cover the cost of development and have a beneficial effect on the future profitability of the company. The directors are concerned about the effect that the expenditure on developing the new product will have on future profits, given that it will take some time between commencing the project and commercial production.

Task

Explain how the costs of developing the new lawnmower will be reflected in the future financial statements of the company.

4.16 The directors of Oak plc are reviewing the accounting treatment for their assets under IAS 36, *Impairment of Assets.*

Prepare brief notes for the directors of Oak plc to answer the following points:

(a) State how, according to IAS 36, an impairment loss is calculated and which two figures are needed.

(b) Explain what is meant by each of these amounts.

(c) State how an impairment loss is to be treated in the financial statements.

4.17 The directors of Beech plc are reviewing their assets under IAS 38, *Intangible Assets.*

Prepare brief notes for the directors of Beech plc to answer the following points:

(a) What is the definition of an intangible asset?

(b) Give **two** examples of an intangible asset.

(c) State and explain the **three** key elements of an intangible asset.

5 Accounting for liabilities and the statement of profit or loss

5.1 Barrios Limited has a corporation tax charge of £25,000 based on its profits for the current year. Where is this recognised in the year-end financial statements?

(a)	In the statement of profit or loss and other comprehensive income only	
(b)	In the statement of profit or loss and other comprehensive income and as a non-current liability in the statement of financial position	
(c)	In the statement of profit or loss and other comprehensive income and as a current liability in the statement of financial position	
(d)	As a current liability in the statement of financial position only	

5.2 The corporation tax charge of Cole Ltd based on its current year profits is £45,000. The company had under-estimated its corporation tax liability for the previous year by £2,000.

What will be the corporation tax charge and the corporation tax liability recognised in the financial statements of Cole Ltd at the end of the current accounting period?

	Corporation tax charge £	Corporation tax liability £	
(a)	47,000	45,000	
(b)	45,000	47,000	
(c)	45,000	43,000	
(d)	43,000	45,000	

5.3 The corporation tax charge of Rossini Ltd based on its current year profits is £12,500. The company had over-estimated its corporation tax liability for the previous year by £2,000.

What will be the corporation tax charge and the corporation tax liability recognised in the financial statements of Rossini Ltd at the end of the current accounting period?

	Corporation tax charge £	Corporation tax liability £	
(a)	14,500	12,500	
(b)	12,500	10,500	
(c)	10,500	12,500	
(d)	14,500	14,500	

5.4 Under IAS 17, *Leases*, how should finance leases be recognised as liabilities on a lessee's statement of financial position?

(a) At the lower of cost and net realisable value of the asset being leased	
(b) At the lower of the fair value of the asset being leased and the present value of the minimum lease payments	
(c) At the higher of the fair value of the asset being leased and its value in use	
(d) At the carrying amount of the asset being leased	

5.5 With reference to IAS 37, *Provisions, Contingent Liabilities and Contingent Assets*, you are to:

(a) Define:

- Provisions.

- Contingent liabilities.

- Contingent assets.

(b) Explain for each the accounting treatment, if any, in the year-end financial statements.

5.6 A business prepares its financial statements to 31 December each year. The following events took place after 31 December but before the date on which the financial statements were authorised for issue:

1   A significant part of the business is to be discontinued.

2   The net realisable value of inventories is found to be materially below the cost price used in the financial statements.

Which of the above is likely to be classified as an adjusting event under IAS 10, *Events after the Reporting Period*?

(a) 1 only	
(b) 2 only	
(c) 1 and 2	
(d) neither 1 nor 2	

5.7 A major customer who owes money to a company at the end of the financial year is declared bankrupt before the date of authorising the financial statements for issue. Under IAS 10, *Events after the Reporting Period*, this should be classified as an adjusting event.

True	
False	

5.8 Prepare notes for a meeting with the directors of Cortez Limited to explain the accounting treatment of the following issues:

(a)   A note to the accounts states that there was a fire in the warehouse of the company that occurred after the year-end and resulted in considerable losses of non-current assets and inventories. No adjustment for these losses appears to have been made in the year-end financial statements.

(b)   There is a non-current liability for something called a 'finance lease' in the statement of financial position of the company.

Note: You should make reference, where appropriate, to relevant international financial reporting standards.

5.9 With reference to IFRS 15, *Revenue from Contracts with Customers*, you are to:

(a)   Define revenue.

(b)   Summarise the five-step process to recognise revenue.

6 Statement of cash flows

- A blank photocopiable pro-forma in the format used in AAT Assessments – of the statement of cash flows, is included in the Appendix – it is advisable to enlarge it to full A4 size. Blank workings sheets are also included in the Appendix.

- Pro-formas and workings sheets are also available to download from www.osbornebooks.co.uk.

6.1 Rowan Ltd has a profit before tax of £28,000 for the year and the statement of profit or loss and statement of financial position show the following:

	£
Depreciation	10,000
Finance costs	2,000
Increase in inventories	5,000
Decrease in trade receivables	4,000
Increase in trade payables	6,000

What is the cash generated by operations for the year?

(a) £45,000 inflow	
(b) £15,000 inflow	
(c) £55,000 inflow	
(d) £25,000 inflow	

6.2   Meadow Ltd has a loss before tax of £11,500 for the year and the statement of profit or loss and statement of financial position show the following:

	£
Depreciation	8,000
Finance costs	1,500
Decrease in inventories	4,000
Increase in trade receivables	5,000
Decrease in trade payables	3,000

What is the cash generated by operations for the year?

(a) £14,000 inflow	
(b) £30,000 inflow	
(c) £14,000 outflow	
(d) £6,000 outflow	

6.3   Boughton Ltd has the following items of receipts and payments for the year:

1	Cash received from sales
2	Cash paid to suppliers and employees
3	Interest paid
4	Tax paid
5	Cash received from share issue

How is the net cash from operating activities calculated using the direct method?

(a) $1 + 2 - 3 - 4 + 5$	
(b) $1 - 2 + 3 - 4$	
(c) $1 - 2 - 3 - 4$	
(d) $1 - 2 + 3 + 4 + 5$	

6.4 You have been asked to help prepare the statement of cash flows and statement of changes in equity for Carmen Ltd for the year ended 31 March 20-1.

The most recent statement of profit or loss and statement of financial position (with comparatives for the previous year) of Carmen Ltd are set out below.

Carmen Ltd – Statement of profit or loss for the year ended 31 March 20-1

	£000
Continuing operations	
Revenue	33,040
Cost of sales	−14,270
Gross profit	18,770
Dividends received	30
Loss on disposal of property, plant and equipment	−50
Distribution costs	−10,210
Administrative expenses	−6,340
Profit from operations	2,200
Finance costs	−190
Profit before tax	2,010
Tax	−350
Profit for the year from continuing operations	1,660

	20-1 £000	20-0 £000
Assets		
Non-current assets		
Property, plant and equipment	15,350	13,750
Current assets		
Inventories	8,234	7,146
Trade receivables	6,827	6,954
Cash and cash equivalents	0	135
	15,061	14,235
Total assets	30,411	27,985
EQUITY AND LIABILITIES		
Equity		
Share capital	10,500	10,000
Share premium	1,200	1,000
Retained earnings	8,973	8,363
Total equity	20,673	19,363
Non-current liabilities		
Bank loans	1,800	2,000
	1,800	2,000
Current liabilities		
Trade payables	7,102	6,047
Tax liabilities	350	575
Bank overdraft	486	0
	7,938	6,622
Total liabilities	9,738	8,622
Total equity and liabilities	30,411	27,985

Further information:

- Depreciation for the year was £2,340,000.
- Property, plant and equipment costing £520,000 with accumulated depreciation of £380,000 was sold in the year.
- All sales and purchases were on credit. Other expenses were paid for in cash.
- A dividend of £1,050,000 was paid during the year.

Required:

(a)   Draft a reconciliation of profit before tax to net cash from operating activities for Carmen Ltd for the year ended 31 March 20-1.

(b)   Draft the statement of cash flows for Carmen Ltd for the year ended 31 March 20-1.

(c)   Draft the statement of changes in equity for Carmen Ltd for the year ended 31 March 20-1.

6.5 Set out below are financial statements for Underdesk Limited for the year ending 20-7 and also for the previous year.

Underdesk Limited: Statement of profit or loss for the year ended 31 December

	20-7	20-6
Continuing operations	£000	£000
Revenue	5,490	4,573
Cost of sales	−3,861	−3,201
Gross profit	1,629	1,372
Profit on disposal of PPE	29	13
	1,658	1,385
Distribution costs	−557	−445
Administrative expenses	−428	−297
Profit from operations	673	643
Finance costs	−156	−47
Profit before tax	517	596
Tax	−129	−124
Profit for the year from continuing operations	388	472

Underdesk Limited: Statement of financial position as at 31 December

	20-7	20-6
ASSETS	£000	£000
Non-current assets	5,461	2,979
Current assets		
Inventories	607	543
Trade receivables	481	426
Cash and cash equivalents	−	104
	1,088	1,073
Total assets	6,549	4,052
EQUITY AND LIABILITIES		
Equity		
Share capital	1,400	800
Share premium	400	100
Retained earnings	2,460	2,168
Total equity	4,260	3,068
Non-current liabilities		
Bank loans	1,700	520
	1,700	520
Current liabilities		
Trade payables	371	340
Tax liabilities	129	124
Bank overdraft	89	−
	589	464
Total liabilities	2,289	984
Total equity and liabilities	6,549	4,052

Further information:

- The total depreciation charge for the year was £672,000.

- Property, plant and equipment with a carrying amount of £85,000 was sold in the year.

- All revenue sales and purchases were on credit. Other expenses were paid for in cash.

- A dividend of £96,000 was paid during the year.

Required:

Task 1

Draft a reconciliation of profit before tax to net cash from operating activities for the year ended 31 December 20-7.

Task 2

Draft the statement of cash flows for Underdesk Limited for the year ended 31 December 20-7.

7 Interpretation of financial statements

7.1   A limited company has the following statement of profit or loss:

	£000
Continuing operations	
Revenue	225
Cost of sales	−140
Gross profit	85
Distribution costs	−20
Administrative expenses	−25
Profit from operations	40
Finance costs	−10
Profit before tax	30
Tax	−8
Profit for the year from continuing operations	22

(a)   State the formula that is used to calculate each of the following ratios:

   (1)   Gross profit percentage

   (2)   Distribution costs/revenue percentage

   (3)   Operating profit percentage

   (4)   Interest cover

(b)   Calculate the above ratios (to the nearest one decimal place).

7.2   The following information is taken from the statement of financial position of a limited company.

	£000
Inventories	380
Trade receivables	450
Cash and cash equivalents	40
Trade payables	410
Non-current liabilities	320
Share capital	450
Retained earnings	140
Further information:	
Revenue for year	4,390
Cost of sales for year	3,360

(a)   State the formula that is used to calculate each of the following ratios:

   (1)   Current ratio

   (2)   Acid test (quick) ratio

   (3)   Inventory turnover

   (4)   Inventory holding period

   (5)   Trade receivables collection period

   (6)   Trade payables payment period

   (7)   Gearing

(b)   Calculate the above ratios (to the nearest one decimal place).

7.3 The following information is taken from the financial statements of a limited company.

	£000
Revenue	1,450
Profit from operations	120
Profit after tax	90
Non-current assets	350
Total assets	870
Share capital (£1 ordinary shares)	500
Retained earnings	220
Non-current liabilities	100
Current liabilities	50

(a) State the formula that is used to calculate each of the following ratios:

    (1) Return on capital employed

    (2) Operating profit percentage

    (3) Return on shareholders' funds

    (4) Asset turnover (net assets)

    (5) Asset turnover (non-current assets)

(b) Calculate the above ratios (to the nearest one decimal place).

7.4 Bragg plc wants to acquire a majority holding in a private limited company. The Managing Director of Bragg plc has asked you to analyse the financial statements of two possible companies and to deal with some queries he has about financial statements. He has asked you to consider the profitability of the companies and their financial position. The financial statements of the two companies are set out below and on the next page.

**Summary statements of profit or loss
for the year ended 31 March 20-4**

	Roy Limited	Ishiguro Limited
	£000	£000
Continuing operations		
Revenue	8,483	10,471
Cost of sales	−3,732	−5,026
Gross profit	4,751	5,445
Distribution costs	−1,218	−1,483
Administrative expenses	−903	−1,658
Profit from operations	2,630	2,304
Finance costs	−160	−520
Profit before tax	2,470	1,784
Tax	−593	−428
Profit for the year from continuing operations	1,877	1,356

Statements of financial position as at 31 March 20-4

	Roy Limited	Ishiguro Limited
ASSETS	£000	£000
Non-current assets	6,806	12,579
Current assets		
Inventories	2,531	2,181
Trade receivables	1,054	2,309
Cash and cash equivalents	828	5
	4,413	4,495
Total assets	11,219	17,074
EQUITY AND LIABILITIES		
Equity		
Share capital	2,000	2,000
Share premium	1,000	500
Retained earnings	4,367	4,997
Total equity	7,367	7,497
Non-current liabilities		
Bank loans	2,000	6,500
	2,000	6,500
Current liabilities		
Trade payables	1,259	2,166
Bank overdraft	–	483
Tax liabilities	593	428
	1,852	3,077
Total liabilities	3,852	9,577
Total equity and liabilities	11,219	17,074

Required:

Prepare a report for Bragg plc that includes the following:

(a)   A calculation (to the nearest one decimal place) of the following four ratios of Roy Limited and Ishiguro Limited:

return on shareholders' funds, gross profit percentage, gearing, interest cover

(b)   An explanation of the meaning of each ratio and a comment on the relative profitability and financial position of the two companies based on the ratios calculated.

(c)   A conclusion as to which company to invest in, based only on these ratios and your analysis.

7.5 The directors of Mercia Printers Limited, a medium-sized printing firm, have recently read the industry's trade magazine and seen an article quoting the following average ratios for the printing sector:

Return on capital employed	16%
Gearing	21%
Current ratio	1.8:1
Operating profit percentage	8%
Trade payables payment period	62 days

The magazine article discusses the benefits of printing companies benchmarking their own performance against the sector's industrial average in order to assess overall performance and efficiency.

Mercia Printers Limited's statement of profit or loss and statement of financial position are set out below and on the next page.

Mercia Printers Limited

Statement of profit or loss for the year ended 31 August 20-4

	£000
Continuing operations	
Revenue	2,750
Cost of sales	−2,200
Gross profit	550
Distribution costs	−140
Administrative expenses	−210
Profit from operations	200
Finance costs	−63
Profit before tax	137
Tax	−41
Profit for the year from continuing operations	96

Mercia Printers Limited
Statement of financial position as at 31 August 20-4

ASSETS	£000
Non-current assets	450
Current assets	
Inventories	215
Trade receivables	352
Cash and cash equivalents	13
	580
Total assets	1,030
EQUITY AND LIABILITIES	
Equity	
Share capital	240
Retained earnings	366
Total equity	606
Non-current liabilities	250
	250
Current liabilities	
Trade payables	133
Tax liabilities	41
	174
Total liabilities	424
Total equity and liabilities	1,030

Required:

Write a report for the directors of Mercia Printers Limited, assessing the performance of the company.

The draft report should include:

(a)   A calculation (to the nearest one decimal place) from the financial statements of Mercia Printers Limited of the appropriate ratios listed in the magazine article (see above). You should quote the formulas used and show detailed workings for each ratio.

(b)   An assessment of the company's overall performance, comparing its ratios with the sector average.

8   Consolidated financial statements

> • Blank photocopiable pro-formas in the format used in AAT Assessments – of the consolidated statement of profit or loss, and the consolidated statement of financial position, are included in the Appendix – it is advisable to enlarge them to full A4 size. Blank workings sheets are also included in the Appendix.
>
> • Pro-formas and workings sheets are also available to download from www.osbornebooks.co.uk.

8.1 Wyvern plc invested £260,000 in 150,000 ordinary shares of £1 each in Sidbury Limited. At the date of acquisition the equity of Sidbury Limited comprised £200,000 in share capital and £120,000 in retained earnings.

What is the value of goodwill at the date of acquisition?

(a) £240,000	
(b) £20,000	
(c) £60,000	
(d) £50,000	

8.2 At 31 March 20-1 the equity of Teme Limited comprises £100,000 in share capital and £80,000 in retained earnings. The parent company, Severn plc, currently owns 60,000 of £1 ordinary shares in Teme Limited.

What is the value of the non-controlling interest at 31 March 20-1?

(a) £180,000	
(b) £108,000	
(c) £80,000	
(d) £72,000	

8.3 Star plc owns 70% of the ordinary shares in Buck Limited. Revenue for the year ended 31 March 20-1 is: Star £500,000, Buck £140,000. The revenue of Star plc includes goods sold to Buck Limited for £20,000. All of these goods still remain in the inventory of Buck Limited at the end of the year.

What is the value for revenue that will be shown in the consolidated statement of profit or loss for Star plc and its subsidiary undertaking for the year ended 31 March 20-1?

(a) £640,000	
(b) £661,000	
(c) £620,000	
(d) £626,000	

8.4 IFRS 3, *Business Combinations*, identifies a number of features in the preparation of consolidated financial statements. Explain the following:

- Method of accounting to be used in acquisitions.
- Assets and liabilities acquired.
- Goodwill.

8.5 **(a)** In business combinations, how are fair values to be treated on acquisition?

(b) What effect do fair values have on the calculations for:

- Goodwill.
- Non-controlling interest.
- Post-acquisition profits.

8.6   You have been asked to assist in the preparation of the consolidated financial statements of the Shopan Group. Set out below are the statements of financial position of Shopan Limited and its subsidiary undertaking Hower Limited, as at 30 September 20-9:

Statements of financial position as at 30 September 20-9

	Shopan Limited	Hower Limited
ASSETS	£000	£000
Non-current assets		
Property, plant and equipment	6,273	1,633
Investment in Hower Limited	2,100	
	8,373	1,633
Current assets		
Inventories	1,901	865
Trade receivables	1,555	547
Cash and cash equivalents	184	104
	3,640	1,516
Total assets	12,013	3,149
EQUITY AND LIABILITIES		
Equity		
Share capital	2,000	500
Share premium	950	120
Retained earnings	4,246	1,484
Total equity	7,196	2,104
Non-current liabilities	2,870	400
Current liabilities		
Trade payables	1,516	457
Tax liabilities	431	188
	1,947	645
Total liabilities	4,817	1,045
Total equity and liabilities	12,013	3,149

Further information:

- The share capital of both Shopan Limited and Hower Limited consists of ordinary shares of £1 each.
- Shopan Limited acquired 375,000 of the issued shares and voting rights in Hower Limited on 30 September 20-9.
- The fair value of the non-current assets of Hower Limited at 30 September 20-9 was £2,033,000.
- Shopan Limited has decided non-controlling interest will be valued at their proportionate share of net assets.

Required:

Task 1

Draft the consolidated statement of financial position for Shopan Limited and its subsidiary undertaking as at 30 September 20-9.

Task 2

IFRS 10, *Consolidated Financial Statements*, defines power over an investee as 'existing rights that give the current ability to direct the relevant activities'. Give two of the criteria that, according to IFRS 10, give power over an investee.

8.7 The Finance Director of Fairway plc has asked you to prepare the draft consolidated statement of profit or loss for the group. The company has one subsidiary, Green Limited. The statements of comprehensive income of the two companies, prepared for internal purposes, for the year ended 30 June 20-2 are set out below:

Statements of profit or loss for the year ended 30 June 20-2

	Fairway plc	Green Limited
Continuing operations	£000	£000
Revenue	12,200	4,400
Cost of sales	−8,500	−3,100
Gross profit	3,700	1,300
Distribution costs	−1,600	−500
Administrative expenses	−400	−200
Dividends received from Green Limited	80	–
Profit from operations	1,780	600
Finance costs	−300	−200
Profit before tax	1,480	400
Tax	−400	−100
Profit for the year from continuing operations	1,080	300

Further information:

- Fairway plc acquired 80% of the issued share capital and voting rights of Green Limited on 1 July 20-1.

- During the year Green Limited sold goods which had cost £750,000 to Fairway plc for £1,000,000. All the goods had been sold by Fairway plc by the end of the year.

- Dividends paid during the year were:

    Fairway plc, £700,000

    Green Limited, £100,000

- There were no impairment losses on goodwill during the year.

Required:

Draft a consolidated statement of profit or loss for Fairway plc and its subsidiary undertaking for the year ended 30 June 20-2.

8.8   Perran Plc acquired 80% of the issued share capital and voting rights of Porth Ltd on 1 April 20-0 for £750,000. At that date Porth Ltd had issued share capital of £600,000 and retained earnings of £240,000.

Extracts from the statements of financial position for the two companies one year later at 31 March 20-1 are as follows:

	Perran Plc	Porth Ltd
	£000	£000
ASSETS		
Non-current assets		
Investment in Porth Ltd	750	
Property, plant and equipment	770	800
	1,520	800
Current assets	450	350
Total assets	1,970	1,150
EQUITY AND LIABILITIES		
Equity		
Share capital	1,000	600
Retained earnings	450	300
Total equity	1,450	900
Non-current liabilities	120	50
Current liabilities	400	200
Total liabilities	520	250
Total equity and liabilities	1,970	1,150

Further information:

- In March 20-1, Porth Ltd sold goods costing £20,000 to Perran Plc at a price of £40,000. At 31 March 20-1 three quarters of the goods were unsold by Perran Plc.
- Included within the current assets of Perran Plc and in the current liabilities of Porth Ltd is an inter-company transaction for £70,000 that took place in early March 20-1.
- Perran Plc has decided non-controlling interest will be valued at their proportionate share of net assets.

Required:

Draft the consolidated statement of financial position for Perran Plc and its subsidiary undertaking as at 31 March 20-1.

8.9   Fistral Plc acquired 75% of the issued share capital and voting rights of Beach Ltd on 1 April 20-0.

Extracts from their statements of profit or loss for the year ended 31 March 20-1 are shown below:

	Fistral Plc	Beach Ltd
	£000	£000
Continuing operations		
Revenue	18,250	6,450
Cost of sales	−11,800	−3,100
Gross profit	6,450	3,350
Other income	600	−
Distribution costs and administrative expenses	−3,750	−1,650
Profit before tax	3,300	1,700

Further information:

·   During the year Beach Ltd sold goods which had cost £50,000 to Fistral Plc for £90,000. Half of these goods still remain in inventory at the end of the year.

·   Other income of Fistral Plc consists of a dividend of £400,000 received from Beach Ltd and rental income received from another company.

Required:

Draft the consolidated statement of profit or loss for Fistral Plc and its subsidiary undertaking up to and including the profit before tax line for the year ended 31 March 20-1.

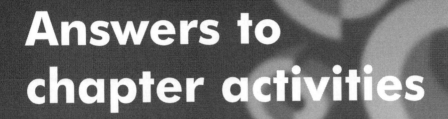

Answers to
chapter activities

1 Purpose of financial statements

1.1 **(a)** According to the *Conceptual Framework for Financial Reporting* the objective of financial reporting is:

- to provide financial information about the reporting entity,
- that is useful to existing and potential investors, lenders and other payables/creditors,
- in making decisions about providing resources to the entity,

(b)

User	Purpose
Existing and potential investors	To enable them to assess how effectively management has fulfilled its stewardship role and to consider information that is useful in taking decisions about their existing investment or potential investment in the entity
Lenders	To assess whether loans will be repaid and related interest will be repaid when due/to help potential lenders decide whether to lend and on what terms
Other payables/creditors	To decide whether to sell to the entity and to assess the likelihood that amounts owing will be paid when due

1.2 (a) income − expenses = profits or losses

1.3 (d) £35,250 = £20,650 + £14,600

1.4

Statement	Characteristic
Financial information that is available to decision-makers in time to be capable in influencing their decisions	Timeliness
Financial information that helps assure users that information is faithfully represented	Verifiability
Users of financial statements are able to identify and understand similarities in, and differences among, items	Comparability
Users of financial statements are presented with information that is classified and characterised clearly and concisely	Understandability

1.5 **(a)** The accounting equation is:

Assets = Equity + Liabilities

The elements are defined as follows:

- Assets – resources controlled by the entity as a result of past events and from which future economic benefits are expected to flow to the entity

- Equity – the residual interest in the assets of the entity after deducting all its liabilities

- Liabilities – present obligations of the entity arising from past events, the settlement of which is expected to result in an outflow from the entity of resources embodying economic benefits

(b) - Profit for the year increases the equity in the accounting equation

- This is matched by an increase in the assets of the business that amount to the difference between assets minus liabilities

1.6 **(a)** The elements that appear in financial statements according to the *Conceptual Framework for Financial Reporting* are:

- Assets
- Equity
- Liabilities
- Income
- Expenses

(b) The elements that appear in the statement of profit or loss and other comprehensive income are:

- Income
- Expenses

Income is increases in economic benefits during the accounting period in the form of inflows or enhancements of assets, or decreases of liabilities that result in increases in equity, other than those relating to contributions from equity participants.

Expenses are decreases in economic benefits during the accounting period in the form of outflows or depletions of assets or incurring of liabilities that result in decreases in equity, other than those relating to distributions to equity participants.

1.7 The relevant fundamental principle is objectivity. An accountant must not allow bias, conflict of interest or the undue influence of others to override professional or business judgements.

1.8 The relevant fundamental principle is confidentiality. An accountant must maintain the confidentiality of information, unless the information is a matter of public knowledge. The requirement to maintain confidentiality includes when the accountant is in a social environment.

1.9 The relevant fundamental principle is professional behaviour. An accountant must be honest and truthful in all dealings so as not to bring the profession into disrepute. In particular, accountants must not make exaggerated claims for the services they offer, the qualifications they have, or the experience they have gained.

1.10

Statement	Fundamental principle
The manager of an accountancy firm arranges appropriate training and supervision for staff	Professional competence and due care
An accountant suggests to a prospective client that the client's current accountants are providing a poor service	Professional behaviour
An accounting report contains a misleading statement	Integrity
An accountant must avoid situations that unduly influence professional judgement	Objectivity
An accountant discusses the financial results of a client's business with friends	Confidentiality

1.11 **(a)** 1 Relevance

2 Faithful representation

(b) **Relevance**

For information to be relevant it must:

- Be capable of making a difference in the decisions made by users

- Have predictive value, which helps users to predict future outcomes

- Have confirmatory value, which helps users to confirm previous evaluations

Faithful representation

For the faithful representation of information it must:

- Correspond to the effect of transactions or events

- As far as possible be complete (to include all information necessary for a user), neutral (without bias), and free from error (no errors in the description or process)

2 Introduction to limited company financial statements

2.1 **(a)** **Public limited company (plc)**

A company may become a public limited company if it has:

- Issued share capital of over £50,000

- At least two members (shareholders) and at least two directors

A public limited company may raise capital from the public on the Stock Exchange or similar markets, but not all do so.

(b) **Private limited company (ltd)**

A private limited company is defined by the Companies Act 2006 as 'any company that is not a public company'.

A private limited company has:

- No minimum requirement for issued share capital

- At least one member (shareholder) and at least one director who may be the sole shareholder

The shares of a private limited company are not traded publicly on the Stock Exchange or similar markets, but are transferable between individuals.

2.2 **(b)** Anyone taking legal action proceeds against the company and not the individual shareholders

2.3 **(a)** Ordinary shares

2.4 **(d)** £55,000

2.5 **Crantock Ltd – Statement of profit or loss for the year ending 31 March 20-2**

	£000
Revenue	2,295
Cost of sales	−1,180
Gross profit	1,115
Administrative expenses	−240
Distribution costs	−500
Profit from operations	375
Finance costs	–
Profit before tax	375
Tax	−65
Profit for the year from continuing operations	310

Workings:

Cost of sales	£000
Opening inventories	160
Purchases	1,200
Closing inventories	−180
Cost of sales =	1,180

Crantock Ltd – Statement of financial position as at 31 March 20-2

ASSETS	£000
Non-current assets	
Property, plant and equipment	1,100
Current assets	
Inventories	180
Trade and other receivables	525
Cash and cash equivalents	75
	780
Total assets	1,880
EQUITY AND LIABILITIES	
Equity	
Share capital	700
Share premium	200
Retained earnings	520
Total equity	1,420
Current liabilities	
Trade and other payables	395
Tax liabilities	65
Total liabilities	460
Total equity and liabilities	1,880

Workings:

Plant and equipment	£000
Plant and equipment – cost	1,600
Accumulated depreciation	–500
Plant and equipment =	1,100

Retained earnings	£000
Retained earnings at 1 April 20-1	350
Profit for the year	310
Dividends paid	–140
Retained earnings =	520

2.6   **Playfair Ltd – Statement of profit or loss for the year ending 31 December 20-3**

	£000
Revenue	2,340
Cost of sales	−1,620
Gross profit	720
Administrative expenses	−210
Distribution costs	−320
Profit from operations	190
Finance costs	−40
Profit before tax	150
Tax	−30
Profit for the year from continuing operations	120

Workings:

Cost of sales	£000
Opening inventories	250
Purchases	1,650
Closing inventories	−280
Cost of sales =	1,620

Administrative expenses	£000
Administrative expenses	110
Increase in allowance for doubtful debts	20
Depreciation: plant and equipment	*80
Administrative expenses =	210

*depreciation: £800 x 20% = £160 ÷ 2 = £80

Distribution costs	£000
Distribution costs	240
Depreciation: plant and equipment	*80
Distribution costs =	320

*depreciation as per administrative expenses

Playfair Ltd – Statement of financial position as at 31 December 20-3

ASSETS	£000
Non-current assets	
Property, plant and equipment	410
Current assets	
Inventories	280
Trade and other receivables	350
Cash and cash equivalents	140
	770
Total assets	1,180
EQUITY AND LIABILITIES	
Equity	
Share capital	380
Share premium	50
Retained earnings	330
Total equity	760
Non-current liabilities	
Loan	200
	200
Current liabilities	
Trade and other payables	190
Tax liabilities	30
	220
Total liabilities	420
Total equity and liabilities	1,180

Workings:

Property, plant and equipment	£000
Plant and equipment – cost	800
Accumulated depreciation – plant and equipment	*–390
Property, plant and equipment =	410

*£230 + £160

Trade and other receivables	£000
Trade and other receivables	350
Prepayments – trial balance	40
Allowance for doubtful debts	–40
Trade and other receivables =	350

Trade and other payables	£000
Trade and other payables	160
Accruals – trial balance	30
Trade and other payables =	190

Retained earnings	£000
Retained earnings at 1 January 20-3	260
Profit for the year	120
Dividends paid	–50
Retained earnings =	330

3 Published financial statements of limited companies

3.1 'The objective of financial statements is to provide **information** about the **financial** position, financial **performance** and **cash** flows of an entity that is **useful** to a wide range of **users** in making **economic** decisions.'

3.2 (c)   1, 2 and 4

3.3 (d)   (1) nine months   (2) six months

3.4 (c)   1 and 3

3.5 (a)   1

3.6 **(a)** **Wymark Ltd – Statement of profit or loss and other comprehensive income for the year ended 31 March 20-4**

	£000
Revenue	10,884
Cost of sales	−7,655
Gross profit	3,229
Distribution costs	−1,100
Administrative expenses	−544
Profit from operations	1,585
Finance costs	−200
Profit before tax	1,385
Tax	−348
Profit for the year from continuing operations	1,037
Other comprehensive income for the year	500
Total comprehensive income for the year	1,537

Workings:

Cost of sales	£000
Opening inventories	2,043
Purchases	7,854
Closing inventories	−2,422
Depreciation	*180
Cost of sales =	7,655

*depreciation: buildings £1,500 x 2% x 50% = £15; plant and equipment (£2,722 − £1,402) x 25% x 50% = £165; total £180

Distribution costs	£000
Distribution costs	980
Accrual	12
Depreciation	*108
Distribution costs =	1,100

*depreciation as per cost of sales, but at 30%

Administrative expenses	£000
Administrative expenses	461
Irrecoverable debts	11
Depreciation	*72
Administrative expenses =	544

*depreciation as per cost of sales, but at 20%

(b) **Wymark Ltd – Statement of changes in equity for the year ended 31 March 20-4**

	Share capital	Share premium	Revaluation surplus	Retained earnings	Total equity
	£000	£000	£000	£000	£000
Balance at 1 April 20-3	3,500	0		1,457	4,957
Changes in equity					
Total comprehensive income			500	1,037	1,537
Dividends				−600	−600
Issue of share capital					
Balance at 31 March 20-4	3,500	0	500	1,894	5,894

(c) **Wymark Ltd – Statement of financial position as at 31 March 20-4**

	£000
ASSETS	
Non-current assets	
Property, plant and equipment	5,758
Current assets	
Inventories	2,422
Trade and other receivables	1,833
Cash and cash equivalents	155
	4,410
Total assets	10,168
EQUITY AND LIABILITIES	
Equity	
Share capital	3,500
Revaluation surplus	500
Retained earnings	1,894
Total equity	5,894
Non-current liabilities	
Bank loan	2,500
	2,500
Current liabilities	
Trade and other payables	1,426
Tax liabilities	348
	1,774
Total liabilities	4,274
Total equity and liabilities	10,168

Workings:

Property, plant and equipment	£000
Land and buildings – value	5,500
Accumulated depreciation – land and buildings	*–732
Plant and equipment – cost	2,722
Accumulated depreciation – plant and equipment	**–1,732
Property, plant and equipment =	5,758

*£702 + £30
**£1,402 + £330

Trade and other receivables	£000
Trade and other receivables	1,802
Irrecoverable debts	–11
Prepayments – trial balance	42
Trade and other receivables =	1,833

Trade and other payables	£000
Trade and other payables	1,309
Accruals – trial balance	105
Additional distribution costs accrued	12
Trade and other payables =	1,426

3.7 **(a)** **Nathan Ltd – Statement of profit or loss and other comprehensive income for the year ended 31 March 20-1**

	£000
Revenue	21,495
Cost of sales	–9,331
Gross profit	12,164
Distribution costs	–6,259
Administrative expenses	–4,577
Profit from operations	1,328
Finance costs	–150
Profit before tax	1,178
Tax	–207
Profit for the year from continuing operations	971
Other comprehensive income for the year	0
Total comprehensive income for the year	971

Workings:

Cost of sales	£000
Opening inventories	641
Purchases	9,364
Returns outwards	–47
Closing inventories	–627
Cost of sales =	9,331

Distribution costs	£000
Distribution costs	3,852
Accrual	22
Depreciation	*2,385
Distribution costs =	6,259

*depreciation: plant and equipment (£20,500 – £4,600) x 25% x 60% = £2,385

Administrative expenses	£000
Administrative expenses	2,975
Irrecoverable debts	12
Depreciation	*1,590
Administrative expenses =	4,577

*depreciation as per distribution costs, but at 40%

(b) **Nathan Ltd – Statement of changes in equity for the year ended 31 March 20-1**

	Share capital £000	Share premium £000	Revaluation surplus £000	Retained earnings £000	Total equity £000
Balance at 1 April 20-0	6,000	1,000	0	2,537	9,537
Changes in equity					
Total comprehensive income				971	971
Dividends				–450	–450
Balance at 31 March 20-1	6,000	1,000	0	3,058	10,058

(c) **Nathan Ltd – Statement of financial position as at 31 March 20-1**

	£000
ASSETS	
Non-current assets	
Property, plant and equipment	11,925
Current assets	
Inventories	627
Trade and other receivables	1,720
Cash and cash equivalents	110
	2,457
Total assets	14,382
EQUITY AND LIABILITIES	
Equity	
Share capital	6,000
Share premium	1,000
Retained earnings	3,058
Total equity	10,058
Non-current liabilities	
Bank loan	3,000
	3,000
Current liabilities	
Trade and other payables	1,117
Tax liabilities	207
	1,324
Total liabilities	4,324
Total equity and liabilities	14,382

Workings:

Property, plant and equipment	*£000*
Plant and equipment – cost	20,500
Accumulated depreciation – plant and equipment	*-8,575
Property, plant and equipment =	11,925

*£4,600 + £3,975

Trade and other receivables	*£000*
Trade and other receivables	1,546
Irrecoverable debts	-12
Prepayments – trial balance	186
Trade and other receivables =	1,720

Trade and other payables	*£000*
Trade and other payables	1,010
Accruals – trial balance	85
Additional distribution costs accrued	22
Trade and other payables =	1,117

4 Accounting for assets

4.1 Task 1

Two criteria for recognition of an item of PPE:

- It is probable that **future economic benefits** will flow to the entity
- The cost of the asset can be **measured reliably**

Task 2

(a) Cost is the purchase price of the asset, including any import duties, plus any costs directly attributable to bring the asset to the location and condition for its intended use, plus the estimated costs of dismantling and removing the asset at the end of its useful life.

(b) Attributable costs which can be included in the cost of an asset

Two from:

- Costs of site preparation
- Initial delivery and handling costs
- Installation and assembly costs
- Costs of testing the asset
- Professional fees, eg engineers, architects

(c) Costs which cannot be included in the cost of an asset

Two from:

- Administration and other general overhead costs
- Start-up costs of a new business or section of the business
- Start-up costs for introducing a new product or service – such as advertising and promotional costs

(d) Two models to choose from:

- **Cost model** – the asset is carried at cost less accumulated depreciation and impairment losses
- **Revaluation model** – the asset is carried at a revalued amount, being its fair value less any subsequent depreciation and impairment losses; revaluations are to be made regularly to ensure that the carrying amount does not differ materially from its fair value at the date of the statement of financial position.

4.2 **(a)** IAS 16, *Property, Plant and Equipment*, defines depreciation as the systematic allocation of the depreciable amount of an asset over its useful life. (Depreciable amount is the cost or valuation of the asset, less any residual value.)

(b) • IAS 16 states that, initially, PPE are to be measured at cost in the statement of financial position.

• After acquisition of PPE an entity must choose either the cost model or the revaluation model as its accounting policy – which is then applied to an entire class of PPE.

• Using the cost model, assets are carried in the statement of financial position at cost less accumulated depreciation and impairment losses.

• Using the revaluation model, assets are carried at a revalued amount, being fair value less any subsequent depreciation and impairment losses; revaluations are to be made regularly to ensure that the carrying amounts do not differ materially from fair values at the date of the statement of financial position.

• The residual value and the useful life of an asset are to be reviewed at least annually.

• Depreciation continues to be recognised even if the fair value of an asset exceeds its carrying amount (but there is no need for depreciation when the residual value is greater than the carrying amount).

• Spending money on repair and maintenance of an asset does not remove the need for depreciation.

• When calculating depreciable amount, the residual values of assets are often low or immaterial – for example, the scrap value of a machine is often negligible.

• Depreciation can be applied to separate parts of an asset where each part is a significant cost – for example, the engines of an aircraft are often depreciated separately from the body of the aircraft.

• Depreciation for the period is recognised in the statement of profit or loss and other comprehensive income (unless it is included in the carrying amount of another asset).

• When determining the useful life of an asset, the following factors need to be considered (even if the asset is not being used):

– expected usage of the asset, ie the expected capacity or output

– expected physical wear and tear, which depends on operational factors and the repair and maintenance programme

– technical or commercial obsolescence, eg the introduction of new technology, changes in demand for the product or service

– legal or similar limits on the use of the asset, eg the period for which an asset is leased

4.3   (b)   The entity has no specific aim or application for the intangible asset

4.4   (a)   Reliability

4.5   **(a)**   IAS 38, *Intangible Assets*, defines an intangible asset as:
- An identifiable non-monetary asset
- Without physical substance

(b)   Before an intangible asset arising from development is recognised as an intangible asset in the financial statements of Tanhosier Ltd they would have to demonstrate:
- The technical feasibility of completing the intangible asset so that it will be available for use or sale
- The intention to complete the intangible asset and to use or sell it
- Its ability to use or sell the intangible asset
- The way in which the intangible asset will generate probable future economic benefits
- The availability of resources to complete the development and to use or sell the intangible asset
- Its ability to measure reliably the expenditure attributable to the intangible asset

4.6   (d)   1, 3, and 4

Note that IAS 36 does not apply to current assets, such as inventories.

4.7 **Task 1**

External indicators

Two from:

- A significant fall in the asset's market value
- Adverse effects on the entity caused by technology, markets, the economy, laws
- Increases in interest rates
- The stock market value of the entity is less than the carrying amount of net assets

Internal indicators

Two from:

- Obsolescence or physical damage to the asset
- Adverse effects on the asset of a significant reorganisation within the entity
- The economic performance of the asset is worse than expected

Note: Other indicators – such as evidence from internal financial statements – can indicate that an asset may be impaired.

Examples include:

- A fall in the profit (or an increase in the loss) from operations
- A fall in the cash flows from operations, or a negative cash flow
- A fall in budgeted cash flows, or budgeted profit from operations

Task 2

(a) An impairment review involves comparing the asset's carrying amount with the recoverable amount.

(b) An impairment review is carried out in three steps:

Step 1 Identify the asset's carrying amount (ie cost/revaluation less depreciation/amortisation to date)

Step 2 Identify the asset's recoverable amount, ie the higher of fair value less costs of disposal (the net realisable value of the asset) and value in use (the present value of the future cash flows expected to be derived from the asset, including cash from its ultimate disposal).

Step 3 If carrying amount is greater than recoverable amount, then the asset is impaired and should be written down to its recoverable amount in the statement of financial position. The amount of the impairment loss is recognised as an expense in the statement of profit or loss and other comprehensive income unless it relates to a previously revalued asset, when it is recognised as a decrease in other comprehensive income and is debited to the revaluation surplus within equity (to the extent of the revaluation surplus for that particular asset).

4.8   (c)   1 and 3

4.9   (b)   £1,700

4.10   **(a)**   The recoverable amount is the higher of the fair value (market value), less costs of disposal, and the value in use.

Fair value is the price that would be received to sell an asset in an orderly transaction between market participants at the measurement date.

Value in use is the present value of the future cash flows expected to be derived from an asset.

Recoverable amount is the higher of:

Fair value less costs of disposal   £120,000 – £3,000 = £117,000

Value in use   £122,000 = Recoverable amount

(b)   An impairment loss is the amount by which the carrying amount of an asset exceeds its recoverable amount.

Carrying amount £220,000 – £95,000 =   £125,000

Recoverable amount   =   £122,000

Impairment Loss   =   £3,000

4.11

Year	Finance charge
	£
20-1	1,500
20-2	1,200
20-3	900
20-4	600
20-5	300

4.12 **(a)** IAS 17, *Leases*, sets out the following:

'A finance lease is a lease that transfers substantially all the risks and rewards incidental to ownership of an asset'.

'An operating lease is a lease other than a finance lease'.

(b) **(1)** At the commencement of the lease term a finance lease should be recognised as an asset in the statement of financial position, together with a corresponding liability to the lessor, at an amount equal to the lower of:

– the fair value of the item, and

– the present value of the minimum lease payments

(2) Lease payments under an operating lease are recognised as an expense in the statement of profit or loss and other comprehensive income on a straight-line basis over the lease term (unless another basis is more representative of the time pattern of the user's benefit).

(c) As the lease period of the first lease is for the major part of the economic life of the asset, and the present value of the minimum lease payments amounts to substantially all of the fair value of the leased asset, it should be classified as a finance lease. This is not the case for the second lease which should therefore be accounted for as an operating lease.

4.13 **(a)** The two inventory valuation methods allowed by IAS 2, *Inventories*, are:

- FIFO (first in, first out) assumes that those items bought first are the first to be used in production or selling.

- AVCO (average cost), or weighted average cost method whereby the average cost of items held at the beginning of any period is calculated and, as the inventories are issued for production or selling purposes, all items are issued at that average price. When new inventory is received, the average issue price will then need to be recalculated.

(b) LIFO (last in, first out) cannot be used under IAS 2.

4.14 (b) At the lower of cost and net realisable value

4.15 IAS 38, *Intangible Assets*, sets out the accounting treatment for expenditure on research and development.

The costs of developing the new lawnmower are likely to be classified, for the purpose of the financial statements, as development costs. Such costs are either recognised as an expense in the statement of profit or loss and other comprehensive income when they are incurred, or they may be capitalised (ie recognised on the statement of financial position) as an intangible asset. In order to apply the latter treatment, Lawnderer Limited must be able to demonstrate all of the following criteria given by IAS 38:

- The technical feasibility of completing the intangible asset so that it will be available for use or sale

- Its intention to complete the intangible asset and to use or sell it

- Its ability to use or sell the intangible asset

- The way in which the intangible asset will generate probable future economic benefits

- The availability of resources to complete the development and to use or sell the intangible asset

- Its ability to measure the development expenditure reliably

The project would appear to fulfil all of the criteria, subject to the resource of finance being available either from the company's bank or from shareholders willing to invest more capital.

If all of the criteria are met then the costs of the development may be capitalised and carried on the statement of financial position as an intangible asset until such time as the project commences commercial production. The intangible asset will then be amortised over its useful life against future profits. The effect of this is that the development costs will not affect profits until production commences and sales are made.

4.16 (a) An impairment loss is the amount by which the carrying amount of an asset exceeds its recoverable amount. The loss is calculated as the difference between the asset's recoverable amount and its carrying amount.

(b) 'Carrying amount' is the amount at which an asset is recognised in the statement of financial position after deducting any accumulated depreciation (amortisation) and accumulated impairment losses.

'Recoverable amount' of an asset is the higher of its fair value, less costs of disposal, and its value in use. The latter is the present value of the future cash flows expected to be derived from the asset, including cash from its ultimate disposal.

(c) The value of the asset is reduced to its recoverable amount in the statement of financial position and the impairment loss is recognised immediately in the statement of comprehensive income (unless it relates to a previously revalued asset, when it is recognised as a decrease in other comprehensive income and is debited to the revaluation surplus within equity).

4.17 **(a)** An identifiable non-monetary asset without physical substance.

(b) 1 Computer software

2 Patents

Note: other examples include copyrights, customer lists, licences and marketing rights

(c) 1 **Identifiability** – the asset is either separable from the entity and is capable of being sold or transferred, or it arises from contractual or other legal rights.

2 **Control** – the entity has the power to obtain future economic benefits from the asset.

3 **Future economic benefits** – includes revenue from the sale of products or services, cost savings, or other benefits.

5 Accounting for liabilities and the statement of profit or loss

5.1 (c) In the statement of profit or loss and other comprehensive income and as a current liability in the statement of financial position

5.2 (a) 47,000   45,000

5.3 (c) 10,500   12,500

5.4 (b) At the lower of the fair value of the asset being leased and the present value of the minimum lease payments

5.5 **(a)** • A **provision** is a liability of uncertain timing or amount

• A **contingent liability** is:

– either a possible obligation arising from past events whose existence will be confirmed only by the occurrence or non-occurrence of one or more uncertain future events not wholly within the entity's control

– or a present obligation that arises from past events but is not recognised because:

(1) either it is not probable that an outflow of economic benefits will be required to settle the obligation

(2) or the obligation cannot be measured with sufficient reliability

• A **contingent asset** is a possible asset arising from past events whose existence will be confirmed only by the occurrence or non-occurrence of one or more uncertain future events not wholly within the entity's control.

(b) • A **provision** is to be recognised as a liability in the financial statements when:

– an entity has a present obligation as a result of a past event

– it is probable that an outflow of economic benefits will be required to settle the obligation

– a reliable estimate can be made of the amount of the obligation

Note that the word 'probable' used in IAS 37 means that there is a more than 50% likelihood of occurrence of the obligation.

A provision should also be disclosed as a note to the financial statements, giving:

– details of changes in the amount of provisions between the beginning and end of the year

– a description of the provision(s) and expected timings of any resulting transfers

– an indication of the uncertainties regarding the amount or timing of any resulting transfers

A **contingent liability** is not recognised in the financial statements; however, it should be disclosed as a note to the financial statements which includes:

– a brief description of the nature of the contingent liability

– an estimate of its financial effect

– an indication of the uncertainties relating to the amount or timing of any outflow

– the possibility of any reimbursement

Note that a contingent liability is a 'possible' obligation, ie a less than 50% likelihood of its occurrence.

Where a contingent liability is considered to be remote, then no disclosure is required in the notes to the financial statements.

A **contingent asset** is not recognised in the financial statements. It is disclosed only where an inflow of economic benefits is probable; disclosure in the notes to the financial statements should include:

– a brief description of the nature of the contingent asset

– an estimate of its financial effect

5.6   (b)   2 only

5.7   True

5.8   **Notes for the directors of Cortez Limited**

   (a)   The fire at the warehouse and the subsequent losses that resulted are a non-adjusting event under IAS 10, *Events after the Reporting Period*. These are events that take place after the financial statements have been prepared at the year end and before the time when the statements are authorised for issue to interested parties. Provision is required in the year-end accounts only for adjusting events which are events that provide evidence of conditions that existed at the end of the reporting period. Non-adjusting events should be disclosed if they are of such materiality that non-disclosure would affect the ability of the users of financial statements to reach a proper understanding of the financial position of the company. As this event is disclosed in a note to the accounts it meets these criteria.

   (b)   The company will have entered into a lease for non-current assets, such as machinery or vehicles. Cortez Limited is the lessee and the lessor will, most likely, be a finance company.

   As it is a finance lease, it is a longer term lease, under which substantially all of the risks and rewards of ownership are transferred to the lessee.

   The non-current liability is the amount of the finance lease – shown at the lower of the fair value of the asset being leased and the present value of the minimum lease payments. There may also be a current liability showing on the statement of financial position for the amount of the finance lease payments due within the next 12 months.

   The non-current assets section of the statement of financial position will indicate the asset(s) being leased.

5.9   **(a)**   IFRS 15, *Revenue from Contracts with Customers*, defines revenue as income arising in the course of an entity's ordinary activities.

   (b)   The five step process:

Step 1	identify the contract with the customer
Step 2	identify the performance obligations in the contract
Step 3	determine the transaction price
Step 4	allocate the transaction price to the performance obligations in the contract
Step 5	recognise revenue when a performance obligation is satisfied

6 Statement of cash flows

6.1 (a) £45,000 inflow

6.2 (d) £6,000 outflow

6.3 (c) 1 – 2 – 3 – 4, ie cash received from sales, minus cash paid to suppliers and employees, minus interest paid, minus tax paid.

6.4 **(a)**

Carmen Ltd – Reconciliation of profit before tax to net cash from operating activities	
	£000
Profit before tax	2,010
Adjustments for:	
Depreciation	2,340
Dividends received	–30
Loss on disposal of property, plant and equipment	50
Finance costs	190
Adjustment in respect of inventories	–1,088
Adjustment in respect of trade receivables	127
Adjustment in respect of trade payables	1,055
Cash generated by operations	4,654
Tax paid	–575
Interest paid	–190
Net cash from operating activities	3,889

(b)

Carmen Ltd – Statement of cash flows for year ended 31 March 20-1	
	£000
Net cash from operating activities	3,889
Investing activities	
Dividends received	30
Proceeds on disposal of property, plant and equipment	90
Purchases of property, plant and equipment	–4,080
Net cash used in investing activities	–3,960
Financing activities	
Bank loans repaid	–200
Proceeds of share issue	700
Dividends paid	–1,050
Net cash used in financing activities	–550
Net increase/decrease in cash and cash equivalents	–621
Cash and cash equivalents at beginning of year	135
Cash and cash equivalents at end of year	–486

(c)   **Carmen Ltd – Statement of changes in equity for the year ended 31 March 20-1**

	Share capital	Share premium	Revaluation surplus	Retained earnings	Total equity
	£000	£000	£000	£000	£000
Balance at 1 April 20-0	10,000	1,000	0	8,363	19,363
Changes in equity					
Profit for the year				1,660	1,660
Dividends				−1,050	−1,050
Issue of share capital	500	200	0		700
Balance at 31 March 20-1	10,500	1,200	0	8,973	20,673

Workings:

Proceeds on disposal of property, plant and equipment	£000
Carrying amount of PPE sold	*140
Loss on disposal	−50
Total disposal proceeds =	90

*cost price £520, accumulated depreciation −£380 = carrying amount £140

Purchases of property, plant and equipment	£000
PPE at start of year	13,750
Depreciation charge	−2,340
Carrying amount of PPE sold	−140
PPE at end of year	−15,350
Total PPE additions =	−4,080*

*outflow of cash

Dividends received

In AAT Assessments, dividends received are classed as investing activities. Note that IAS 7, *Statement of Cash Flows*, does permit dividends (and also interest) to be classified as operating or investing or financing activities – how they are classified should be applied consistently in a company's financial statements.

6.5 **Task 1**

UNDERDESK LIMITED	
Reconciliation of profit before tax to net cash from operating activities for the year ended 31 December 20-7	
	£000
Profit before tax	517
Adjustments for:	
Depreciation	672
Profit on disposal of property, plant and equipment	–29
Finance costs	156
Adjustment in respect of inventories (607–543)	–64
Adjustment in respect of trade receivables (481–426)	–55
Adjustment in respect of trade payables (371–340)	31
Cash generated by operations	1,228
Interest paid	–156
Tax paid	–124
Net cash from operating activities	948

Task 2

UNDERDESK LIMITED	
Statement of cash flows for the year ended 31 December 20-7	
	£000
Net cash from operating activities	948
Investing activities	
Purchase of property, plant and equipment	–3,239
Proceeds on disposal of property, plant and equipment	114
Net cash used in investing activities	–3,125
Financing activities	
Proceeds of share issue	900
New bank loans	1,180
Dividends paid	–96
Net cash from financing activities	1,984
Net decrease in cash and cash equivalents	–193
Cash and cash equivalents at beginning of year	104
Cash and cash equivalents at end of year	–89

Workings:

Proceeds on disposal of property, plant and equipment	£000
Carrying amount of PPE sold	85
Profit on disposal	29
Total disposal proceeds	114

Purchases of property, plant and equipment	£000
PPE at start of year	2,979
Depreciation charges	−672
Carrying amount of PPE sold	−85
PPE at end of year	−5,461
Total property, plant and equipment additions =	3,239

7 Interpretation of financial statements

7.1

Ratio	(a) Formula	(b) Calculation of ratio (amounts in £000)
(1) Gross profit percentage	$\dfrac{\text{Gross profit}}{\text{Revenue}} \times 100$	$\dfrac{85}{225} \times 100 = 37.8\%$
(2) Distribution costs/revenue percentage	$\dfrac{\text{Distribution costs} \times 100}{\text{Revenue}}$	$\dfrac{20}{225} \times 100 = 8.9\%$
(3) Operating profit percentage	$\dfrac{\text{Profit from operations}}{\text{Revenue}} \times 100$	$\dfrac{40}{225} \times 100 = 17.8\%$
(4) Interest cover	$\dfrac{\text{Profit from operations}}{\text{Finance costs}}$	$\dfrac{40}{10} = 4 \text{ times}$

7.2

Ratio	(a) Formula	(b) Calculation of ratio (amounts in £000)
(1) Current ratio	$\dfrac{\text{Current assets}}{\text{Current liabilities}}$	$\dfrac{870}{410}$ = 2.1:1
(2) Acid test (quick) ratio	$\dfrac{\text{Current assets – inventories}}{\text{Current liabilities}}$	$\dfrac{870 - 380}{410}$ = 1.2:1
(3) Inventory turnover	$\dfrac{\text{Cost of sales}}{\text{Inventories}}$	$\dfrac{3,360}{380}$ = 8.8 times
(4) Inventory holding period	$\dfrac{\text{Inventories}}{\text{Cost of sales}} \times 365 \text{ days}$	$\dfrac{380}{3,360}$ x 365 = 41.3 days
(5) Trade receivables collection period	$\dfrac{\text{Trade receivables}}{\text{Revenue}} \times 365 \text{ days}$	$\dfrac{450}{4,390}$ x 365 = 37.4 days
(6) Trade payables payment period	$\dfrac{\text{Trade payables}}{\text{Cost of sales}} \times 365 \text{ days}$	$\dfrac{410}{3,360}$ x 365 = 44.5 days
(7) Gearing	$\dfrac{\text{Non-current liabilities}}{\text{Non-current liabilities + total equity}} \times 100$	$\dfrac{320}{320 + 590}$ x 100 = 35.2%

7.3

Ratio	(a) Formula	(b) Calculation of ratio (amounts in £000)
(1) Return on capital employed	$\dfrac{\text{Profit from operations}}{\text{Total equity + Non-current liabilities}}$ x 100	$\dfrac{120}{720 + 100}$ x 100 = 14.6%
(2) Operating profit percentage	$\dfrac{\text{Profit from operations}}{\text{Revenue}}$ x 100	$\dfrac{120}{1,450}$ x 100 = 8.3%
(3) Return on share-holders' funds	$\dfrac{\text{Profit after tax}}{\text{Total equity}}$ x 100	$\dfrac{90}{720}$ x 100 = 12.5%
(4) Asset turnover (net assets)	$\dfrac{\text{Revenue}}{\text{Total assets – current liabilities}}$	$\dfrac{1,450}{870 - 50}$ = 1.8 times
(5) Asset turnover (non-current assets)	$\dfrac{\text{Revenue}}{\text{Non-current assets}}$	$\dfrac{1,450}{350}$ = 4.1 times

7.4

REPORT

To:	Managing Director, Bragg Plc	From:	AAT student
Subject:	Interpretation of ratios	Date:	Today

Introduction

This report has been prepared to assist in the interpretation of the financial statements of Roy Limited and Ishiguro Limited, the possible private limited companies in which you are considering the purchase of a majority holding. The report considers the profitability and the financial position of each of the companies for the year ended 31 March 20-4, and compares the results between them.

(a) Calculation of the ratios (amounts in £000)

Ratio	Roy Limited		Ishiguro Limited	
Return on shareholder's funds	$\dfrac{1,877}{7,367}$	= 25.5%	$\dfrac{1,356}{7,497}$	= 18.1%
Gross profit percentage	$\dfrac{4,751}{8,483}$	= 56.0%	$\dfrac{5,445}{10,471}$	= 52.0%
Gearing	$\dfrac{2,000}{2,000 + 7,367}$	= 21.4%	$\dfrac{6,500}{6,500 + 7,497}$	= 46.4%
Interest cover	$\dfrac{2,630}{160}$	= 16.4 times	$\dfrac{2,304}{520}$	= 4.4 times

(b) Explanation and comment

Return on shareholders' funds:

- this ratio measures the percentage of profit after tax available for shareholders that is generated by the use of equity finance
- the return on shareholders' funds of Roy Limited is higher than that of Ishiguro Limited
- this means that more profits for shareholders are generated from an investment in Roy Limited
- thus an investment in Roy Limited is initially more attractive

Gross profit percentage:

- this ratio shows in percentage terms how much gross profit is being generated by the revenue of the company
- the gross profit percentage of Roy Limited is higher than that of Ishiguro Limited

- this indicates that the underlying business in Roy Limited is more profitable than that in Ishiguro Limited
- thus Roy Limited is relatively more attractive than Ishiguro Limited

Gearing:

- gearing measures the percentage of non-current liabilities to non-current liabilities + total equity
- the gearing percentage in Ishiguro Limited is higher than that in Roy Limited
- this indicates that Ishiguro Limited is more reliant on debt than is Roy Limited; Ishiguro Limited is a riskier company to invest in than Roy Limited; there is the risk that Ishiguro may not generate sufficient profits to maintain the dividend to ordinary shareholders; it may fail to meet interest payments from profits if there is a downturn in profitability
- the greater risk to ordinary shareholders makes Ishiguro Limited a relatively less attractive investment

Interest cover:

- this ratio shows how many times the company could meet its finance costs out of profit from operations
- Ishiguro Limited has lower interest cover than Roy Limited
- this means that Ishiguro Limited may have more difficulty than Roy Limited in meeting finance costs out of profits; however, there is still a reasonable margin for comfort as Ishiguro can meet the finance costs four times over at the current level of profits
- nevertheless, Roy Limited is still a more attractive investment as the risk of defaulting on finance costs is very low

(c) Conclusion

- The ratios show that Roy Limited is a relatively more attractive investment than Ishiguro Limited
- Roy Limited is the more profitable company with a higher return on shareholders' funds and higher gross profit percentage
- Roy Limited has a more secure financial position – being lower geared with a much higher interest cover than Ishiguro Limited; this suggests that returns to shareholders from investing in Roy Limited are less risky than those of Ishiguro Limited
- My overall recommendation, on the basis of the ratios calculated and analysis performed, is that Bragg Limited should invest in Roy Limited rather than in Ishiguro Limited

7.5 **(a)** **Mercia Printers Limited**
(amounts in £000)

Industry average

Return on capital employed

$$\frac{\text{Profit from operations}}{\text{Total equity + Non-current liabilities}} \times 100 \qquad \frac{200}{606 + 250} \times 100 = 23.4\% \qquad 16\%$$

Gearing

$$\frac{\text{Non-current liabilities}}{\text{Non-current liabilities + Total equity}} \times 100 \qquad \frac{250}{250 + 606} \times 100 = 29.2\% \qquad 21\%$$

Current ratio

$$\frac{\text{Current assets}}{\text{Current liabilities}} \qquad \frac{580}{174} \times 100 = 3.3{:}1 \qquad 1.8{:}1$$

Operating profit percentage

$$\frac{\text{Profit from operations}}{\text{Revenue}} \times 100 \qquad \frac{200}{2,750} \times 100 = 7.3\% \qquad 8\%$$

Trade payables payment period

$$\frac{\text{Trade payables}}{\text{Cost of sales}} \times 365 \qquad \frac{133}{2,200} \times 365 = 22.1 \text{ days} \qquad 62 \text{ days}$$

(b)

To: The Directors

From: AAT student

Date: Today

Report on Mercia Printers Limited performance and efficiency for the year ended 31 August 20-4

The company has appeared to utilise its capital far more profitably than its competitors. Its **return on capital employed** of 23.4% is much better than the industry average of 16%. Therefore, from a profit and investment point of view, the company is very favourably placed.

Gearing is a measure of risk – it reflects the balance between non-current liabilities and non-current liabilities + total equity. Here the company reports 29.2% against an industry average of 21%. The company has proportionately more money tied up in non-current borrowed funds than is the norm in this industry sector. However 29.2% is still relatively low (gearing in excess of 50% indicates a high-geared company) and there is the possibility that more funds could be borrowed to finance future growth and expansion.

The **current ratio** measures the short-term day-to-day financing (liquidity) of the business. Here the company has £3.30 of current assets to cover every £1.00 worth of current liabilities. This is a healthy margin, and is proof that the company does not suffer from any cash flow problems. The ratio is well in excess of the industry average of 1.8.

The **operating profit percentage** measures the profitability of the business. The company reports 7.3% against an industry average of 8%, so it is under-performing in this area. The company could look into its pattern of expenditure to see if any economies can be made which would increase profit and bring it back in line with the sector average. Key items of expenditure in this area are wages and salaries and advertising. The company could also look to reducing its cost of sales – reducing the price it pays for paper, for example.

The **trade payables payment period** measures the average amount of time it takes for the company to pay its suppliers. Here it is paying very promptly with a result of 22.1 days against a sector average of 62 days. It might be suggested that the company could benefit its cash by extending the terms it obtains from suppliers, especially as liquidity is not a problem.

In conclusion, the company performs better than the sector average in three out of the five ratios. The areas which could be investigated are gearing (which, although higher than the industry norm, is still relatively low), and profitability (where the return is below the industry norm by almost 1%).

8 Consolidated financial statements

8.1 (b) £20,000

8.2 (d) £72,000

8.3 (c) £620,000

8.4
- **Method of accounting to be used in acquisitions**

  The acquisition method is to be used. This measures the cost of the identifiable assets and liabilities being acquired and usually results in the recognition of goodwill.

- **Assets and liabilities acquired**

  The identifiable assets and liabilities being acquired are identified and valued at their fair value on the date of acquisition.

- **Goodwill**

  Goodwill is an asset representing future economic benefits arising from other assets acquired in a business combination that are not individually identified and separately recognised. Goodwill is tested annually for impairment under IAS 36.

  Negative goodwill is where the cost of the acquisition is less than the fair value of assets and liabilities acquired. IFRS 3 says that, where negative goodwill is indicated, the first step should be to check the values used to ensure that they are correct. Negative goodwill is recognised in the statement of profit or loss and other comprehensive income immediately.

8.5 **(a)** IFRS 3, *Business Combinations*, requires that the cost of the business acquired is to be measured at the fair values of all the identifiable* assets and liabilities that existed at the date of acquisition.

Fair value is the price that would be received to sell an asset or paid to transfer a liability in an orderly transaction between market participants at the measurement date. For example, the fair value of land and buildings would be the market value, for plant and equipment it would also be the market value, for raw materials it would be the current replacement cost.

The procedure for dealing with fair values is to restate the subsidiary's statement of financial position using fair values. Increases in the valuation of assets are credited to revaluation reserve; decreases are debited to revaluation reserve. Any changes to the value of liabilities are also passed through revaluation reserve. Note that, to be dealt with in this way, the fair value of identifiable assets and liabilities must be capable of being measured reliably.

*identifiable = either separable from the entity (eg capable of being sold) or arising from contractual or other legal rights.

(b) Fair value has an effect on the calculations for goodwill, non-controlling interest (where applicable), and sometimes on post-acquisition profits:

- Goodwill, which is the cost of the investment in the subsidiary, less the fair value of the subsidiary's identifiable assets and liabilities

- Non-controlling interest, which is the proportion of the subsidiary, based on the fair value of the subsidiary's identifiable assets and liabilities

- Post-acquisition profits, which will be affected where the use of fair value for non-current assets leads to a different depreciation charge from that based on historic costs

8.6   Task 1

Shopan Limited: Consolidated statement of financial position as at 30 September 20-9

	£000
ASSETS	
Non-current assets	
Goodwill	222
Property, plant and equipment	8,306
	8,528
Current assets	
Inventories	2,766
Trade receivables	2,102
Cash and cash equivalents	288
	5,156
Total assets	13,684
EQUITY AND LIABILITIES	-
Equity	
Share capital	2,000
Share premium	950
Retained earnings	4,246
Non-controlling interest	626
Total equity	7,822
Non-current liabilities	3,270
Current liabilities	
Trade payables	1,973
Tax liabilities	619
	2,592
Total liabilities	5,862
Total equity and liabilities	13,684

Workings:

1   Shopan Limited holding in Hower Limited

$$\frac{375,000}{500,000} \qquad = 75\%$$

Non-controlling interest

$$\frac{125,000}{500,000} \qquad = 25\%$$

2   Revaluation of non-current assets to fair value:

Property, plant and equipment	£000
Consolidated PPE prior to fair value adjustment	7,906
Adjustment to fair value	400
	8,306

3   Calculation of goodwill arising on consolidation and non-controlling interest:

Goodwill	£000
Consideration	2,100
NCI at acquisition	*626
Net assets acquired	−2,504
Goodwill =	222

*£2,104 net assets + £400 revaluation = £2,504 x 25%

4   Calculation of non-controlling interest:

Non-controlling interest (NCI)	£000
Share capital – attributable to NCI	125
Share premium – attributable to NCI	30
Revaluation surplus – attributable to NCI	100
Retained earnings – attributable to NCI	371
Non-controlling interest =	626

Task 2

According to IFRS 10, *Consolidated Financial Statements*, power to direct the relevant activities of the investee include:

- Rights in the form of voting rights of an investee (eg a majority – above 50 per cent – of the voting rights – although there may be circumstances where such ownership does not give power).

- Rights to appoint, reassign or remove members of an investee's key management personnel who have the ability to direct the relevant activities.

- Rights to appoint or remove another entity that directs the relevant activities.

- Rights to direct the investee to enter into, or veto any changes to, transactions for the benefit of the investor.

- Other rights (eg decision-making rights specified in a management contract) that give the ability to direct the relevant activities.

8.7   **Fairway plc and its subsidiary**

Consolidated statement of profit or loss for the year ended 30 June 20-2

Continuing operations	£000
Revenue	15,600
Cost of sales	−10,600
Gross profit	5,000
Distribution costs	−2,100
Administrative expenses	−600
Profit from operations	2,300
Finance costs	−500
Profit before tax	1,800
Tax	−500
Profit for the year from continuing operations	1,300

Workings:

Attributable to	£000
Equity holders of the parent £1,300 − £60	1,240
Non-controlling interest 20% x £300*	60
Profit for the period from continuing operations =	1,300

*Green's after-tax profit for the year

Revenue	£000
Fairway plc	12,200
Green Ltd	4,400
Total inter-company adjustment	−1,000
Revenue =	15,600

Cost of sales	£000
Fairway plc	8,500
Green Ltd	3,100
Total inter-company adjustment*	−1,000
Cost of sales =	10,600

*purchases −£1,000 = cost of sales −£1,000

8.8 **(a)** **Perran plc – Consolidated statement of financial position as at 31 March 20-1**

	£000
ASSETS	
Non-current assets	
Goodwill	78
Property, plant and equipment	1,570
	1,648
Current assets	
Inventories	
Trade receivables	
Cash and cash equivalents	
	*715
Total assets	2,363
EQUITY AND LIABILITIES	
Equity	
Share capital	1,000
Share premium	–
Retained earnings	486
Non-controlling interest	177
Total equity	1,663
Non-current liabilities	170
Current liabilities	**530
Total liabilities	700
Total equity and liabilities	2,363

*£450 + £350 – £70 intercompany transaction – £15 reduction in inventory to cost = £715

**£400 + £200 – £70 intercompany transaction = £530

Workings:

Goodwill	£000
Consideration	750
NCI at acquisition	168
Net assets acquired	–840
Goodwill =	78

Non-controlling interest (NCI)	£000
Share capital – attributable to NCI	120
Retained earnings – attributable to NCI	*57
Non-controlling interest =	177

*£300 – £15 unrealised profit = £285 x 20% = £57

Retained earnings	£000
Perran Plc	450
Porth Ltd – attributable to Perran Plc	**36
Retained earnings =	486

**£300 – £240 – £15 unrealised profit = £45 x 80% = £36

Note: The unrealised profit of £15,000 is deducted from the statement of profit or loss of Porth before calculating the NCI at the date of the consolidated statements of financial position; £15,000 is also deducted from the inventory of Perran

8.9

Fistral Plc – Consolidated statement of profit or loss for the year ended 31 March 20-1.	
	£000
Continuing operations	
Revenue	24,610
Cost of sales	−14,830
Gross profit	9,780
Other income	200
Distribution costs and administrative expenses	−5,400
Profit before tax	4,580

Workings:

Revenue	£000
Fistral Plc	18,250
Beach Ltd	6,450
Total inter-company adjustment	−90
Revenue =	24,610

Cost of sales	£000
Fistral Plc	11,800
Beach Ltd	3,100
Total inter-company adjustment*	−70
Cost of sales =	14,830

* purchases −£90, unrealised profit £20[+] = cost of sales −£70

[+] unrealised profit is deducted from closing inventories; the effect of this is to increase cost of sales (because closing inventories are deducted in the cost of sales calculation)

Distribution costs and administrative expenses

£3,750,000 + £1,650,000 = £5,400,000

Profit before tax

£3,300,000 + £1,700,000 − £400,000 inter-company dividend − £20,000 unrealised profit

= £4,580,000

Practice
assessment 1

The Practice Assessment contains eight tasks and you should attempt to complete every task.

Each task is independent. You will not need to refer to your answers to previous tasks.

Read every task carefully to make sure you understand what is required.

In tasks 1, 2 and 6 you will see there are tables that can be used for your workings for your pro-formas. You don't have to use the workings tables to achieve full marks in these tasks, but any data entered into the workings tables will be taken into consideration if you make errors in the main pro-forma.

Where the date is relevant, it is given in the task data.

Both minus signs and brackets can be used to indicate negative numbers unless task instructions say otherwise.

You must use a full stop to indicate a decimal point. For example, write 100.57 NOT 100,57 or 100 57

You may use a comma to indicate a number in the thousands, but you don't have to. For example 10000 and 10,000 are both acceptable.

Task 1

You have been asked to prepare the financial statements of Hanjoy Ltd for the year ended 31 March 20-1. The company's trial balance as at 31 March 20-1 and further information is shown below.

Hanjoy Ltd

Trial balance as at 31 March 20-1

	Debit	Credit
	£000	£000
Share capital		100,000
Revaluation surplus at 1 April 20-0		20,000
Trade and other payables		9,854
Land and buildings – value/cost	125,500	
– accumulated depreciation at 1 April 20-0		15,000
Plant and equipment – cost	40,000	
– accumulated depreciation at 1 April 20-0		14,400
Trade and other receivables	17,234	
Accruals		256
5% bank loans repayable 20-9		20,000
Cash and cash equivalents	7,901	
Retained earnings at 1 April 20-0		9,280
Interest paid	1,000	
Sales revenue		100,497
Purchases	60,191	
Distribution costs	15,348	
Administrative expenses	11,627	
Inventories at 1 April 20-0	8,486	
Dividends paid	2,000	
	289,287	289,287

Further information:

- The inventories at the close of business on 31 March 20-1 cost £9,107,000.

- Land, which is not depreciated, is included in the trial balance at a value of £50,500,000. It is to be revalued at £60,000,000 and this revaluation is to be included in the financial statements for the year ended 31 March 20-1.

- Depreciation is to be provided for the year to 31 March 20-1 as follows:
  Buildings　　　　　　　　　2% per annum　　　Straight-line basis
  Plant and equipment　　　20% per annum　　Reducing (diminishing) balance basis

- Depreciation is to be apportioned as follows:

	%
Cost of sales	50
Distribution costs	20
Administrative expenses	30

- Trade receivables include a debt of £12,000 which is to be written off. Bad (irrecoverable) debts are to be classified as administrative expenses.

- Distribution costs of £35,000 owing at 31 March 20-1 are to be provided for.

- The corporation tax charge for the year has been calculated as £1,827,000.

- All of the operations are continuing operations.

Required:

(a)   Draft the statement of profit or loss and other comprehensive income for Hanjoy Ltd for the year ended 31 March 20-1. Use the layout shown below.

(b)   Draft the statement of changes in equity for Hanjoy Ltd for the year ended 31 March 20-1. Use the layout shown on the next page.

Note: You will be asked to draft a statement of financial position in Task 2 using the same data.

(a)   **Hanjoy Ltd – Statement of profit or loss and other comprehensive income
for the year ended 31 March 20-1**

	£000
Revenue	
Cost of sales	
Gross profit	
Distribution costs	
Administrative expenses	
Profit from operations	
Finance costs	
Profit before tax	
Tax	
Profit for the year from continuing operations	
Other comprehensive income for the year	
Total comprehensive income for the year	

Workings:

Cost of sales	£000
Cost of sales =	

Distribution costs	£000
Distribution costs =	

Administrative expenses	£000
Administrative expenses =	

(b)   Hanjoy Ltd – Statement of changes in equity for the year ended 31 March 20-1

	Share capital £000	Share premium £000	Revaluation reserve £000	Retained earnings £000	Total equity £000
Balance at 1 April 20-0					
Changes in equity					
Total comprehensive income					
Dividends					
Issue of share capital					
Balance at 31 March 20-1					

Task 2

This task is a continuation of the scenario in Task 1. The same data is used, to which please refer.

You have been asked to prepare the statement of financial position for Hanjoy Ltd as at 31 March 20-1.

Draft the statement of financial position for Hanjoy Ltd as at 31 March 20-1.

Hanjoy Ltd – Statement of financial position as at 31 March 20-1

	£000
ASSETS	
Non-current assets	
Current assets	
Total assets	
EQUITY AND LIABILITIES	
Equity	
Total equity	
Non-current liabilities	
Current liabilities	
Total liabilities	
Total equity and liabilities	

Workings:

Property, plant and equipment	£000
Property, plant and equipment =	

Trade and other receivables	£000
Trade and other receivables =	

Trade and other payables	£000
Trade and other payables =	

Retained earnings	£000
Retained earnings =	

Revaluation surplus	£000
Revaluation surplus =	

Task 3

You are an AAT student working for Omega Accountants. You have been asked to prepare the financial statements of Foss Ltd, a manufacturer of children's toys, for the year ended 31 December 20-1.

Enter your answers regarding the following matters in the box provided.

Matter 1

During the year Foss Ltd has replaced an old machine with a new machine.

Explain to the directors why the new machine is recognised as an asset for the statement of financial position.

Identify two measurement bases which should be used to determine the amount at which the machine should be recognised in the financial statements.

Matter 2

At a business event in your city a bank manager looking for new business asks you to let her have a copy of Foss Ltd's most recent financial statements. You know that Foss Ltd banks with a different bank.

Identify and explain the relevant fundamental principle in accordance with the AAT's Code of Professional Ethics.

Matter 1

Matter 2

Task 4

Plant Ltd operates a chain of garden centres. The company's Finance Director is working on the financial statements for the year ended 31 December 20-1, and has brought the following matters to your attention.

(1)   Three years ago, Plant Ltd revalued a piece of land from a cost of £500,000 to its market value of £600,000. There has been a decline in the property market and in September 20-1 the market value of the land was £450,000.

(2)   Plant Ltd is being sued by a former employee following an accident at work. The company will have to pay substantial damages if it loses the case. The company's lawyers advise that it is probable that the company will lose the case, and have estimated that damages of approximately £100,000 will have to be paid.

Explain, with reasons, how each of the items above should be treated in Plant Ltd's financial statements for the year ended 31 December 20-1, using the figures from above to illustrate your answer where possible.

Task 5

This task consists of one true/false question and four multiple-choice questions.

(a)   A finance lease is where there is no substantial transfer of the risks and rewards of ownership to the lessee.

True	
False	

(b)   Which one of the following statements best describes the valuation of inventories under IAS 2, *Inventories* at the end of the financial year?

(a)	At the lower of FIFO and AVCO	
(b)	At the lower of cost and net realisable value	
(c)	At the higher of FIFO and AVCO	
(d)	At the higher of cost and net realisable value	

(c)   A business prepares its financial statements to 31 December each year. The following events took place after 31 December but before the date on which the financial statements were authorised for issue:

1   A significant part of the business is to be discontinued.

2   The net realisable value of inventories is found to be materially below the cost price used in the financial statements.

Which of the above is likely to be classified as a non-adjusting event under IAS 10, *Events after the Reporting Period*?

(a)	1 only	
(b)	2 only	
(c)	1 and 2	
(d)	neither 1 nor 2	

(d)   Under IAS 16, *Property, Plant and Equipment*, which of the following costs can be included on initial recognition of property, plant and equipment?

1   Cost of testing the asset

2   Installation and assembly costs

3   Purchase price

4   Initial delivery and handling costs

(a)	1 and 2	
(b)	2 and 3	
(c)	3 and 4	
(d)	All of them	

(e)   Tang Ltd had a profit before tax of £26,000 for the year and the statements of profit or loss and financial position show the following:

	£
Depreciation	12,000
Decrease in inventories	4,000
Increase in trade and other receivables	7,000
Increase in trade and other payables	3,000
Tax paid	9,000

In its statement of cash flows prepared in accordance with IAS 7, what is the amount of Tang's cash from operating activities?

(a)	£40,000	
(b)	£29,000	
(c)	£37,000	
(d)	£51,000	

Task 6

Bravo Plc acquired 75% of the issued share capital and voting rights of Salvo Ltd on 1 April 20-0 for £1,600,000. At that date Salvo Ltd had issued share capital of £1,000,000 and retained earnings of £480,000.

Extracts from the statements of financial position for the two companies one year later at 31 March 20-1 are as follows:

	Bravo Plc	Salvo Ltd
	£000	£000
Assets		
Investment in Salvo Ltd	1,600	
Property, plant and equipment	2,050	1,620
Current assets	1,400	390
Total assets	5,050	2,010
Equity and liabilities		
Equity		
Share capital	2,000	1,000
Retained earnings	1,900	640
Total equity	3,900	1,640
Non-current liabilities	350	220
Current liabilities	800	150
Total liabilities	1,150	370
Total equity and liabilities	5,050	2,010

Further information:

- Included within the current assets of Bravo Plc and in the current liabilities of Salvo Ltd is an inter-company transaction for £50,000 that took place in early March 20-1.

- Bravo Plc has decided non-controlling interest will be valued at their proportionate share of net assets.

(a) Draft the consolidated statement of financial position for Bravo Plc and its subsidiary undertaking as at 31 March 20-1. Use the layout shown below.

Bravo Plc – Consolidated statement of financial position as at 31 March 20-1

	£000
ASSETS	
Non-current assets	
Goodwill	
Property, plant and equipment	
Current assets	
Inventories	
Trade receivables	
Cash and cash equivalents	
Total assets	
EQUITY AND LIABILITIES	
Equity	
Share capital	
Share premium	
Retained earnings	
Non-controlling interest	
Total equity	
Non-current liabilities	
Current liabilities	
Total liabilities	
Total equity and liabilities	

Workings:

Goodwill	£000
Goodwill =	

Non-controlling interest (NCI)	£000
Non-controlling interest =	

Retained earnings	£000
Retained earnings =	

Weiss Plc acquired 80% of the issued share capital and voting rights of Hirsh Ltd on 1 April 20-0. Extracts from their statements of profit or loss for the year ended 31 March 20-1 are shown below:

	Weiss Plc £000	Hirsh Ltd £000
Continuing operations		
Revenue	30,400	10,300
Cost of sales	−17,800	−6,100
Gross profit	12,600	4,200
Other income	700	−
Distribution costs	−3,000	−1,000
Administrative expenses	−1,500	−800
Profit before tax	8,800	2,400

Further information:

- During the year Hirsh Ltd sold goods which had cost £40,000 to Weiss Plc for £100,000. Half of these goods still remain in inventory at the end of the year.
- Other income of Weiss Plc consists of a dividend of £500,000 received from Hirsh Ltd and rental income received from another company.

(b) Draft the consolidated statement of profit or loss for Weiss Plc and its subsidiary undertaking up to and including the profit before tax line for the year ended 31 March 20-1. Use the layout shown below.

Weiss Plc – Consolidated statement of profit or loss for the year ended 31 March 20-1

	£000
Continuing operations	
Revenue	
Cost of sales	
Gross profit	
Other income	
Distribution costs	
Administrative expenses	
Profit from operations	
Finance costs	
Profit before tax	

Workings:

Revenue	£000
Parent	
Subsidiary	
Total inter-company adjustment*	
Revenue =	

*enter '0' if no adjustment needed

Cost of sales	£000
Parent	
Subsidiary	
Total inter-company adjustment*	
Cost of sales =	

*enter '0' if no adjustment needed

Task 7

You have been asked to calculate ratios for Nelson Ltd in respect of its financial statements for the year ending 31 March 20-1 to assist your manager in his analysis of the company.

Nelson Ltd's statement of profit or loss and statement of financial position are set out below and on the next page.

Nelson Ltd – Statement of profit or loss for the year ended 31 March 20-1

	£000
Continuing operations	
Revenue	32,400
Cost of sales	–17,982
Gross profit	14,418
Distribution costs	–7,319
Administrative expenses	–4,345
Profit from operations	2,754
Finance costs	–459
Profit before tax	2,295
Tax	–531
Profit for the year from continuing operations	1,764

Nelson Ltd – Statement of financial position as at 31 March 20-1

	£000
ASSETS	
Non-current assets	
Property, plant and equipment	49,369
Current assets	
Inventories	1,684
Trade receivables	2,833
Cash and cash equivalents	114
	4,631
Total assets	54,000
EQUITY AND LIABILITIES	
Equity	
Share capital	35,000
Retained earnings	15,400
Total equity	50,400
Non-current liabilities	
Bank loans	1,495
	1,495
Current liabilities	
Trade payables	1,574
Tax liabilities	531
	2,105
Total liabilities	3,600
Total equity and liabilities	54,000

Using the form on the next page:

(a) State the formulas that are used to calculate each of the following ratios:

    (1) Return on shareholders' funds

    (2) Current ratio

    (3) Asset turnover (net assets)

    (4) Gearing

    (5) Interest cover

(b) Calculate the above ratios (to the nearest one decimal place).

Ratio	(a) Formula	(b) Calculation of ratio for Nelson Ltd
(1) Return on share-holders' funds		
(2) Current ratio		
(3) Asset turnover (net assets)		
(4) Gearing		
(5) Interest cover		

Task 8

Steve Horan is a shareholder in Blenheim Ltd and has asked you to assist him in assessing the efficiency and effectiveness of the management of the company. You have calculated the following ratios in respect of Blenheim Ltd's financial statements for the last two years to assist you in your analysis.

	20-1	20-0
Gross profit percentage	42.0%	45.0%
Operating profit percentage	9.5%	7.5%
Inventory holding period	84 days	66 days
Trade receivables collection period	55 days	40 days
Trade payables payment period	50 days	42 days

Prepare a report to Steve that includes:

(a) A comment on the relative performance of the company for the two years based on the ratios calculated and what this tells you about the company.

REPORT

To: Steve Horan
From: AAT student
Subject: Shareholding in Blenheim Ltd
Date: Today

if required, continue on next page

(b) Advise, with reasons based on the ratios you have calculated, on whether or not Steve should maintain his investment in the company.

Practice
assessment 2

The Practice Assessment contains eight tasks and you should attempt to complete every task.

Each task is independent. You will not need to refer to your answers to previous tasks.

Read every task carefully to make sure you understand what is required.

In tasks 1, 2 and 6 you will see there are tables that can be used for your workings for your pro-formas. You don't have to use the workings tables to achieve full marks in these tasks, but any data entered into the workings tables will be taken into consideration if you make errors in the main pro-forma.

Where the date is relevant, it is given in the task data.

Both minus signs and brackets can be used to indicate negative numbers unless task instructions say otherwise.

You must use a full stop to indicate a decimal point. For example, write 100.57 NOT 100,57 or 100 57

You may use a comma to indicate a number in the thousands, but you don't have to. For example 10000 and 10,000 are both acceptable.

Task 1

You have been asked to prepare the statement of cash flows and statement of changes in equity for Kneale Ltd for the year ended 31 March 20-1.

The most recent statement of profit or loss and statement of financial position (with comparatives for the previous year) for Kneale Ltd are set out below.

Kneale Ltd – Statement of profit or loss for the year ended 31 March 20-1

	£000
Continuing operations	
Revenue	108,000
Cost of sales	−80,500
Gross profit	27,500
Profit on disposal of property, plant and equipment	112
Distribution costs	−11,214
Administrative expenses	−14,618
Profit from operations	1,780
Finance costs	−693
Profit before tax	1,087
Tax	−214
Profit/Loss for the year from continuing operations	873

Kneale Ltd – Statements of financial position as at 31 March

	20-1 £000	20-0 £000
Assets		
Non-current assets		
Property, plant and equipment	7,610	6,325
Current assets		
Inventories	2,544	2,795
Trade receivables	3,728	3,419
Cash and cash equivalents	0	312
	6,272	6,526
Total assets	13,882	12,851
EQUITY AND LIABILITIES		
Equity		
Share capital	2,500	1,500
Share premium	410	210
Retained earnings	6,566	6,043
Total equity	9,476	7,753
Non-current liabilities		
Bank loans	750	2,500
	750	2,500
Current liabilities		
Trade payables	3,025	2,107
Tax liabilities	214	491
Bank overdraft	417	0
	3,656	2,598
Total liabilities	4,406	5,098
Total equity and liabilities	13,882	12,851

Further information:

- The total depreciation charge for the year was £727,000.
- Property, plant and equipment costing £225,000 with accumulated depreciation of £152,000 was sold in the year.
- All sales and purchases were on credit. Other expenses were paid for in cash.
- A dividend of £350,000 was paid during the year.

(a) Draft a reconciliation of profit before tax to net cash from operating activities for Kneale Ltd for the year ended 31 March 20-1. Use the layout shown on the next page.

(b) Draft the statement of cash flows for Kneale Ltd for the year ended 31 March 20-1. Use the layout shown on page 113.

Note: You will be asked to draft a statement of changes in equity in Task 2 using the same data.

(a)   Kneale Ltd

Reconciliation of profit before tax to net cash from operating activities

	£000
Adjustments for:	
Cash generated by operations	
Net cash from operating activities	

(b) **Kneale Ltd**

Statement of cash flows for the year ended 31 March 20-1

	£000
Net cash from operating activities	
Investing activities	
Net cash used in investing activities	
Financing activities	
Net cash used in financing activities	
Net increase/decrease in cash and cash equivalents	
Cash and cash equivalents at beginning of year	
Cash and cash equivalents at end of year	

Workings:

Proceeds on disposal of property, plant and equipment	*£000*
Total disposal proceeds =	

Purchases of property, plant and equipment	*£000*
Total property, plant and equipment additions =	

Task 2

This task is a continuation of the scenario in Task 1. The same data is used, to which please refer.

You have been asked to prepare the statement of changes in equity for Kneale Ltd for the year ended 31 March 20-1.

Draft the statement of changes in equity for Kneale Ltd for the year ended 31 March 20-1.

Kneale Ltd – Statement of changes in equity for the year ended 31 March 20-1

	Share capital	Share premium	Revaluation surplus	Retained earnings	Total equity
	£000	*£000*	*£000*	*£000*	*£000*
Balance at 1 April 20-0					
Changes in equity					
Total comprehensive income					
Dividends					
Issue of share capital					
Balance at 31 March 20-1					

Task 3

You are an AAT student working for Blenheim Accountants.

Matter 1

You have been asked to prepare the financial statements of Brayford Ltd, a book publisher, for the year ended 31 December 20-1.

During the year Brayford Ltd printed more books than previously and there is a large sum owed by Brayford to the printer.

Explain to the directors why the trade payable amount owed to the printer is recognised as a liability for the statement of financial position.

Identify two measurement bases which should be used to determine the amount at which the trade payable should be recognised in the financial statements.

Matter 2

Another client of Blenheim Accountants is Towan Ltd, a boat builder.

As a result of cash flow problems Towan Ltd has been very slow in paying its trade payables. Having recently completed the financial statements of Towan Ltd you are aware that the cash flow problem remains. The directors ask you to provide a letter which assures the suppliers of Towan Ltd that all future payments will be made on time in accordance with normal trade terms.

Identify and explain the relevant fundamental principle in accordance with the AAT's Code of Professional Ethics.

Enter your answers regarding these matters in the box below.

Matter 1

Matter 2

Task 4

Print Ltd is a manufacturer of computer printers. The company's Finance Director is working on the financial statements for the year ended 31 December 20-1, which have not yet been authorised for issue, and has brought the following matters to your attention.

(1) Print Ltd is about to undertake the development of a new product. The costs of development will be significant and the directors are concerned at the impact that this might have on the company's financial statements.

(2) A major customer of Print Ltd who owed money to the company at 31 December 20-1 has been declared bankrupt.

Explain, with reasons, how each of the items above should be treated in Print Ltd's financial statements for the year ended 31 December 20-1.

Task 5

This task consists of one true/false question and four multiple-choice questions.

(a) In accordance with IAS 37, *Provisions, Contingent Liabilities and Contingent Assets*, a contingent asset should be disclosed in the notes to the financial statements only where the inflow of economic benefits is probable.

True	
False	

(b) A business holds three distinct types of inventory in its warehouse at the end of its financial year. These are valued as follows:

Inventory	FIFO (cost) £	LIFO (cost) £	NRV £
Type R	3,400	3,300	5,200
Type S	1,950	2,050	3,250
Type T	2,600	2,500	2,450
Total	7,950	7,850	10,900

To comply with IAS 2, *Inventories*, indicate the value at which the inventory should be stated in the financial statements.

(a)	£7,700	
(b)	£7,800	
(c)	£7,850	
(d)	£7,950	

(c) Under IAS 17, *Leases*, how should finance leases be recognised as liabilities on a lessee's statement of financial position?

(a) At the higher of fair value less costs to sell and value in use of the asset being leased	
(b) At the higher of the fair value of the asset being leased and the present value of the minimum lease payments	
(c) At the lower of the fair value of the asset being leased and the present value of the minimum lease payments	
(d) At the value in use of the asset being leased	

(d) A limited company has purchased a new machine with the following expenditure:

	£
Invoice price of the machine	18,750
Delivery costs	550
Administration costs	600
Cost of testing the machine	1,100
Total expenditure	21,000

Under IAS 16, *Property, Plant and Equipment*, what cost will the company include in property, plant and equipment?

(a) £19,300	
(b) £19,900	
(c) £20,400	
(d) £21,000	

(e) According to IFRS 15, *Revenue from Contracts with Customers*, how is revenue defined?

(a) Income arising in the course of an entity's ordinary activities	
(b) The amount of cash and cash equivalents received	
(c) Income relating to contributions from equity participants	
(d) The lower of cost and net realisable value of goods or services transferred to customers	

Task 6

Severn Plc acquired 60% of the issued share capital and voting rights of Teme Ltd on 1 April 20-0 for £700,000. At that date Teme Ltd had issued share capital of £700,000 and retained earnings of £250,000.

Extracts from the statements of financial position for the two companies one year later at 31 March 20-1 are as follows:

	Severn Plc £000	Teme Ltd £000
Assets		
Investment in Teme Ltd	700	
Property, plant and equipment	1,800	1,000
Current assets	760	360
Total assets	3,260	1,360
Equity and liabilities		
Equity		
Share capital	2,000	700
Retained earnings	650	310
Total equity	2,650	1,010
Non-current liabilities	120	200
Current liabilities	490	150
Total liabilities	610	350
Total equity and liabilities	3,260	1,360

Further information

- Included within the current assets of Severn Plc and in the current liabilities of Teme Ltd is an inter-company transaction for £20,000 that took place in early March 20-1.
- Severn Plc has decided non-controlling interest will be valued at their proportionate share of net assets.

(a) Draft the consolidated statement of financial position for Severn Plc and its subsidiary undertaking as at 31 March 20-1. Use the layout shown below.

Severn Plc – Consolidated statement of financial position as at 31 March 20-1

	£000
ASSETS	
Non-current assets	
Goodwill	
Property, plant and equipment	
Current assets	
Total assets	
EQUITY AND LIABILITIES	
Equity	
Share capital	
Retained earnings	
Non-controlling interest	
Total equity	
Non-current liabilities	
Current liabilities	
Total liabilities	
Total equity and liabilities	

Workings:

Goodwill	£000
Goodwill =	

Non-controlling interest (NCI)	£000
Non-controlling interest =	

Retained earnings	£000
Retained earnings =	

Sinton Plc acquired 75% of the issued share capital and voting rights of Green Ltd on 1 April 20-0.

Extracts from their statements of profit or loss for the year ended 31 March 20-1 are shown below:

	Sinton Plc	Green Ltd
	£000	£000
Continuing operations		
Revenue	48,400	17,200
Cost of sales	–31,200	–9,800
Gross profit	17,200	7,400
Other income	600	–
Distribution costs	–8,000	–3,200
Administrative expenses	–4,200	–1,000
Profit before tax	5,600	3,200

Further information:

- During the year Green Ltd sold goods which had cost £50,000 to Sinton Plc for £80,000. Two-thirds of these goods still remain in inventory at the end of the year.

- Other income of Sinton Plc consists of a dividend of £500,000 received from Green Ltd and rental income received from another company.

(b) Draft the consolidated statement of profit or loss for Sinton Plc and its subsidiary undertaking up to and including the profit before tax line for the year ended 31 March 20-1. Use the layout shown below.

Sinton Plc – Consolidated statement of profit or loss for the year ended 31 March 20-1

	£000
Continuing operations	
Revenue	
Cost of sales	
Gross profit	
Other income	
Distribution costs	
Administrative expenses	
Profit from operations	
Finance costs	
Profit before tax	

Workings:

Revenue	£000
Parent	
Subsidiary	
Total inter-company adjustment*	
Revenue =	

*enter '0' if no adjustment needed

Cost of sale	£000
Parent	
Subsidiary	
Total inter-company adjustment*	
Cost of sales =	

*enter '0' if no adjustment needed

Task 7

You have been asked to calculate ratios for Laceby Ltd in respect of its financial statements for the year ending 31 March 20-1 to assist your manager in his analysis of the company.

Laceby Ltd's statement of profit or loss and statement of financial position are set out below and on the next page.

Laceby Ltd – Statement of profit or loss for the year ended 31 March 20-1

	£000
Continuing operations	
Revenue	45,300
Cost of sales	−22,620
Gross profit	22,680
Distribution costs	−8,345
Administrative expenses	−10,052
Profit from operations	4,283
Finance costs	−964
Profit before tax	3,319
Tax	−623
Profit for the year from continuing operations	2,696

Laceby Ltd – Statement of financial position as at 31 March 20-1

	£000
ASSETS	
Non-current assets	
Property, plant and equipment	77,094
Current assets	
Inventories	2,514
Trade receivables	3,986
Cash and cash equivalents	1,522
	8,022
Total assets	85,116
EQUITY AND LIABILITIES	
Equity	
Share capital	60,000
Retained earnings	9,685
Total equity	69,685
Non-current liabilities	
Bank loans	12,093
	12,093
Current liabilities	
Trade payables	2,715
Tax liabilities	623
	3,338
Total liabilities	15,431
Total equity and liabilities	85,116

Using the form on the next page:

(a)   State the formulas that are used to calculate each of the following ratios:

  (1)   Gross profit percentage

  (2)   Acid test (quick) ratio

  (3)   Asset turnover (non-current assets)

  (4)   Inventory holding period (days)

  (5)   Trade payables payment period

(b)   Calculate the above ratios (to the nearest one decimal place).

Ratio	(a) Formula	(b) Calculation of ratio for Laceby Ltd
(1) Gross profit percentage		
(2) Acid test (quick) ratio		
(3) Asset turnover (non-current assets)		
(4) Inventory holding period (days)		
(5) Trade payables payment period		

Task 8

Louise Forsythe is a shareholder in Kingham Ltd and has asked you to assist her in assessing the effectiveness of the management of the company in using its resources. You have calculated the following ratios in respect of Kingham Ltd's financial statements for the last two years to assist you in your analysis.

	20-1	20-0
Gross profit percentage	39.0%	42.0%
Operating profit percentage	10.0%	9.5%
Return on shareholders' funds	12.0%	10.5%
Gearing	22.2%	27.4%
Interest cover	10.6 times	9.1 times

Prepare a report to Louise that includes:

(a) A comment on the relative performance of the company for the two years based on the ratios calculated and what this tells you about the company.

REPORT

To: Louise Forsythe
From: AAT student
Subject: Shareholding in Kingham Ltd
Date: Today

if required, continue on next page

(b) Advise, with reasons based on the ratios you have calculated, on whether or not Louise should maintain her investment in the company.

Practice
assessment 3

The Practice Assessment contains eight tasks and you should attempt to complete every task.

Each task is independent. You will not need to refer to your answers to previous tasks.

Read every task carefully to make sure you understand what is required.

In tasks 1, 2 and 6 you will see there are tables that can be used for your workings for your pro-formas. You don't have to use the workings tables to achieve full marks in these tasks, but any data entered into the workings tables will be taken into consideration if you make errors in the main pro-forma.

Where the date is relevant, it is given in the task data.

Both minus signs and brackets can be used to indicate negative numbers unless task instructions say otherwise.

You must use a full stop to indicate a decimal point. For example, write 100.57 NOT 100,57 or 100 57

You may use a comma to indicate a number in the thousands, but you don't have to. For example 10000 and 10,000 are both acceptable.

Task 1

You have been asked to prepare the statement of cash flows and statement of changes in equity for Chen Ltd for the year ended 31 March 20-1.

The most recent statement of profit or loss and statement of financial position (with comparatives for the previous year) of Chen Ltd are set out below and on the next page.

Chen Ltd – Statement of profit or loss for the year ended 31 March 20-1

Continuing operations	£000
Revenue	65,200
Cost of sales	−31,860
Gross profit	33,340
Dividends received	84
Loss on disposal of property, plant and equipment	-40
Distribution costs	−15,627
Administrative expenses	−7,983
Profit from operations	9,774
Finance costs	−212
Profit before tax	9,562
Tax	−3,367
Profit for the year from continuing operations	6,195

Chen Ltd – Statement of financial position as at 31 March 20-1

	20-1	20-0
	£000	£000
ASSETS		
Non-current assets		
Property, plant and equipment	39,630	32,860
Current assets		
Inventories	5,796	4,124
Trade receivables	7,041	6,732
Cash and cash equivalents	0	430
	12,837	11,286
Total assets	52,467	44,146
EQUITY AND LIABILITIES		
Equity		
Share capital	12,000	10,000
Share premium	5,000	4,000
Retained earnings	27,390	21,749
Total equity	44,390	35,749
Non-current liabilities		
Bank loans	1,250	3,000
	1,250	3,000
Current liabilities		
Trade payables	3,176	3,249
Tax liabilities	3,367	2,148
Bank overdraft	284	0
	7,827	5,397
Total liabilities	8,077	8,397
Total equity and liabilities	52,467	44,146

Further information:

- The total depreciation charge for the year was £4,275,000.

- Property, plant and equipment costing £655,000 with accumulated depreciation of £231,000 was sold in the year.

- All sales and purchases were on credit. Other expenses were paid for in cash.

- A dividend of £554,000 was paid during the year.

(a) Draft a reconciliation of profit before tax to net cash from operating activities for Chen Ltd for the year ended 31 March 20-1. Use the layout shown below.

(b) Draft the statement of cash flows for Chen Ltd for the year ended 31 March 20-1. Use the layout shown on the next page.

Note: You will be asked to draft a statement of changes in equity in Task 2 using the same data.

Chen Ltd

Reconciliation of profit before tax to net cash from operating activities

	£000
Adjustments for:	
Cash generated by operations	
Net cash from operating activities	

Chen Ltd

Statement of cash flows for the year ended 31 March 20-1

	£000
Net cash from operating activities	
Investing activities	
Net cash used in investing activities	
Financing activities	
Net cash from financing activities	
Net increase/decrease in cash and cash equivalents	
Cash and cash equivalents at beginning of year	
Cash and cash equivalents at end of year	

Workings:

Proceeds on disposal of property, plant and equipment	*£000*
Total disposal proceeds =	

Purchases of property, plant and equipment	*£000*
Total property, plant and equipment additions=	

Task 2

This task is a continuation of the scenario in Task 1. The same data is used, to which please refer.

You have been asked to prepare the statement of changes in equity for Chen Ltd for the year ended 31 March 20-1.

Draft the statement of changes in equity for Chen Ltd for the year ended 31 March 20-1.

Chen Ltd – Statement of changes in equity for the year ended 31 March 20-1

	Share capital	Share premium	Revaluation surplus	Retained earnings	Total equity
	£000	*£000*	*£000*	*£000*	*£000*
Balance at 1 April 20-0					
Changes in equity					
Total comprehensive income					
Dividends					
Issue of share capital					
Balance at 31 March 20-1					

Task 3

You are an AAT student working for King Accountants. You have been asked to prepare the financial statements of Porth Ltd, a manufacturer of surfboards, for the year ended 31 December 20-1.

Enter your answers regarding the following matters in the box provided.

Matter 1

The directors of Porth Ltd ask why they have to produce "all these financial reports each year" – they say they have better things to do with their time and that the reports are of no use to anyone.

Explain to the directors the objective of general purpose financial reporting according to the IASB's *Conceptual Framework for Financial Reporting*.

Identify from the *Conceptual Framework* the users of financial statements and how they are helped by the information contained in the financial statements.

Matter 2

The directors of Porth Ltd approach you saying that they wish to reduce the company's corporation tax charge to the minimum possible. They ask you to implement ways to achieve this, one suggestion from them being to change the inventory valuation method.

Identify and explain the relevant fundamental principle in accordance with the AAT's Code of Professional Ethics.

Matter 1

Matter 2

Task 4

Carpets Ltd is a manufacturer of carpets. The company's Finance Director is working on the financial statements for the year ended 31 December 20-4, and has brought the following matters to your attention.

(1) Carpets Ltd bought a machine for £340,000 on 1 January 20-1. At that time the useful life of the machine was estimated to be six years and the residual value was estimated at £100,000. The company depreciates machinery on a straight-line basis.

On 1 January 20-4 the residual value of the machine was still considered to be £100,000 but the remaining useful life was reassessed to be four years.

(2) The Finance Director has estimated that Carpets Ltd's corporation tax charge for the year ended 31 December 20-4 is £30,000. In the previous year the company had over-estimated its corporation tax liability by £4,000.

Explain, with reasons, how each of the items above should be treated in Carpets Ltd's financial statements for the year ended 31 December 20-4, using the figures from above to illustrate your answer where possible.

Task 5

This task consists of one true/false question and four multiple choice questions.

(a)   Lopez Ltd has discontinued a significant part of its business after the financial year end of 31 December 20-4 but before the date the financial statements are authorised for issue.

Under IAS 10, *Events after the Reporting Period*, this is an adjusting event.

True	
False	

(b)   Under IAS 1, *Presentation of Financial Statements*, which of the following must be indentified?

1   Going concern

2   Accrual basis of accounting

3   Consistency of presentation

4   Comparative information

(a) None of them	
(b) 1, 2, and 3	
(c) 1, 2 and 4	
(d) All of them	

(c) Hamid Ltd has four assets which the directors wish to test for impairment:

Asset	Carrying amount £	Fair value, less costs of disposal £	Value in use £
1	20,000	21,000	19,000
2	15,000	12,000	14,000
3	33,000	35,000	30,000
4	26,000	22,000	25,000

Which of the above assets is impaired according to IAS 36, *Impairment of Assets*?

(a)	1	
(b)	2	
(c)	1 and 3	
(d)	2 and 4	

(d) IAS 38, *Intangible Assets*, gives three key elements of an intangible asset.

What are the three key elements of an intangible asset?

(a)	identifiability, future economic benefits, control	
(b)	control, reliability, understandability	
(c)	future economic benefits, reliability, comparability	
(d)	identifiability, comparability, reliability	

(e)   AB Ltd has the following year end valuations for the two groups of inventory in which it trades:

	Cost	Net realisable value
	£	£
Inventory A	12,500	18,500
Inventory B	15,000	14,500
Total	27,500	33,000

Under IAS 2, *Inventories*, which **one** of the following valuations is correct?

(a) £27,000	
(b) £27,500	
(c) £33,000	
(d) £33,500	

Task 6

Lee Plc acquired 75% of the issued share capital and voting rights of Shaw Ltd on 1 January 20-0 for £3,400,000. At that date Shaw Ltd had issued share capital of £2,000,000, share premium of £500,000 and retained earnings of £420,000.

Extracts from the statements of financial position for the two companies one year later at 31 December 20-0 are as follows:

	Lee Plc	Shaw Ltd
	£000	£000
ASSETS		
Non-current assets		
Investment in Shaw Ltd	3,550	
Property, plant and equipment	2,745	3,420
	6,295	3,420
Current assets	1,690	1,497
Total assets	7,985	4,917
EQUITY AND LIABILITIES		
Equity		
Share capital	3,500	2,000
Share premium	750	500
Retained earnings	1,390	540
Total equity	5,640	3,040
Non-current liabilities	300	255
Current liabilities	2,045	1,622
Total liabilities	2,345	1,877
Total equity and liabilities	7,985	4,917

Further information:

• Lee Plc has decided non-controlling interest will be valued at their proportionate share of net assets.

• At 1 January 20-0 the fair value of the non-current assets of Shaw Ltd was £200,000 more than the book value. This revaluation has not been recorded in the books of Shaw Ltd (ignore any effect on the depreciation for the year).

• On 1 October 20-0, Lee Plc made an interest-free long-term loan of £150,000 to Shaw Ltd, and classified it as part of its investment in Shaw Ltd. Shaw Ltd has classified the loan as a non-current liability in its Financial Statements. No loan repayments has yet been made.

• The directors of Lee Plc have calculated that goodwill has been impaired by £120,000 during the year.

Draft the consolidated statement of financial position for Lee Plc and its subsidiary undertaking as at 31 December 20-0.

Lee Plc – Consolidated statement of financial position as at 31 December 20-0

	£000
ASSETS	
Non-current assets	
Goodwill	
Property, plant and equipment	
Current assets	
Total assets	
EQUITY AND LIABILITIES	
Equity	
Share capital	
Share premium	
Retained earnings	
Non-controlling interest	
Total equity	
Non-current liabilities	
Current liabilities	
Total liabilities	
Total equity and liabilities	

Workings:

Goodwill	£000
Goodwill =	

Non-controlling interest (NCI)	£000
Non-controlling interest =	

Retained earnings	£000
Retained earnings =	

Property, plant and equipment	£000
Consolidated PPE prior to fair value adjustment	
Adjustment to fair value	

Task 7

You have been given the financial statements of Dodia Ltd for the year ending 31 December 20-0. You are now required to prepare financial ratios to assist your manager in her analysis of the company.

Dodia Ltd's statement of profit or loss and statement of financial position are set out below and on the next page.

Dodia Ltd – Statement of profit or loss for the year ended 31 March 20-0

	£000
Continuing operations	
Revenue	64,300
Cost of sales	–39,163
Gross profit	25,137
Distribution costs	–10,410
Administrative expenses	–7,380
Profit from operations	7,347
Finance costs	–1,054
Profit before tax	6,293
Tax	–2,048
Profit for the year from continuing operations	4,245

Dodia Ltd – Statement of financial position as at 31 March 20-0

	£000
ASSETS	
Non-current assets	
Property, plant and equipment	28,800
Current assets	
Inventories	3,695
Trade receivables	4,568
Cash and cash equivalents	1,075
	9,338
Total assets	38,138
EQUITY AND LIABILITIES	
Equity	
Ordinary share capital	20,000
Retained earnings	10,416
Total equity	30,416
Non-current liabilities	
Bank loans	2,500
	2,500
Current liabilities	
Trade payables	3,174
Tax liabilities	2,048
	5,222
Total liabilities	7,722
Total equity and liabilities	38,138

Note: there have been no share issues during the year.

Using the form below:

(a) State the formulas that are used to calculate each of the following ratios:

    (1) Operating profit percentage

    (2) Acid test (quick) ratio

    (3) Asset turnover (net assets) (times)

    (4) Trade payables payment period (days)

    (5) Interest cover (times)

(b) Calculate the above ratios (to the nearest one decimal place).

Ratio	(a) Formula	(b) Calculation of ratio for Dodia Ltd
(1) Operating profit percentage		
(2) Acid test (quick) ratio		
(3) Asset turnover (net assets) (times)		
(4) Trade payables payment period (days)		
(5) Interest cover (times)		

Task 8

Joanna Fisher, the Managing Director of Faloye Ltd, is concerned that the company is not managing its working capital efficiently. She has sent you an email asking for your assistance in identifying any problem area(s) and for your suggestions as to how these can be remedied.

You have calculated the following ratios in respect of Faloye Ltd's latest financial statements and have also obtained the industry average for each of these for comparative purposes.

	Faloye Ltd	Industry Average
Current ratio	1.6:1	2.1:1
Inventory holding period	37 days	35 days
Trade receivables collection period	38 days	39 days
Trade payables payment period	53 days	44 days

Using the form on the next page prepare an email reply to Joanna that includes:

(a) Comments on whether Faloye Ltd has performed better or worse, in respect of the calculated ratios, as compared to the industry averages.

(b) **Three** suggestions as to how the working capital of Faloye Ltd could be more effectively managed.

email

To:

From:

Subject:

Date:

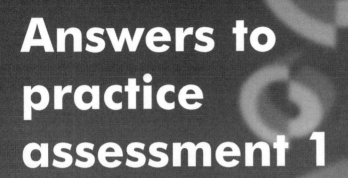

Answers to
practice
assessment 1

Task 1

(a)   Hanjoy Ltd – Statement of profit or loss and other comprehensive income
for the year ended 31 March 20-1

	£000
Revenue	100,497
Cost of sales	−62,880
Gross profit	37,617
Distribution costs	−16,707
Administrative expenses	−13,625
Profit from operations	7,285
Finance costs	−1,000
Profit before tax	6,285
Tax	−1,827
Profit for the year from continuing operations	4,458
Other comprehensive income for the year	9,500
Total comprehensive income for the year	13,958

Workings:

Cost of sales	£000
Opening inventories	8,486
Purchases	60,191
Closing inventories	−9,107
Depreciation	*3,310
Cost of sales =	62,880

*depreciation: buildings £75,000 x 2% x 50% = £750; plant and equipment (£40,000 − £14,400) x 20% x 50% = £2,560; total £3,310

Distribution costs	£000
Distribution costs	15,348
Accrual	35
Depreciation	*1,324
Distribution costs =	16,707

*depreciation as per cost of sales, but at 20%

Administrative expenses	£000
Administrative expenses	11,627
Irrecoverable debts	12
Depreciation	*1,986
Administrative expenses =	13,625

*depreciation as per cost of sales, but at 30%

(b)   **Hanjoy Ltd – Statement of changes in equity for the year ended 31 March 20-1**

	Share capital	Share premium	Revaluation surplus	Retained earnings	Total equity
	£000	£000	£000	£000	£000
Balance at 1 April 20-0	100,000	0	20,000	9,280	129,280
Changes in equity					
Total comprehensive income			9,500	4,458	13,958
Dividends				–2,000	–2,000
Issue of share capital					
Balance at 31 March 20-1	100,000	0	29,500	11,738	141,238

Task 2

Hanjoy Ltd – Statement of financial position as at 31 March 20-1

	£000
Assets	
Non-current assets	
Property, plant and equipment	138,980
Current assets	
Inventories	9,107
Trade and other receivables	17,222
Cash and cash equivalents	7,901
	34,230
Total assets	173,210
EQUITY AND LIABILITIES	
Equity	
Share capital	100,000
Revaluation surplus	29,500
Retained earnings	11,738
Total equity	141,238
Non-current liabilities	
Bank loans	20,000
	20,000
Current liabilities	
Trade and other payables	10,145
Tax liabilities	1,827
	11,972
Total liabilities	31,972
Total equity and liabilities	173,210

Workings:

Property, plant and equipment	£000
Land and buildings – value	125,500
Accumulated depreciation – land and buildings	*–16,500
Revaluation – land and buildings	9,500
Plant and equipment – cost	40,000
Accumulated depreciation – plant and equipment	**–19,520
Property, plant and equipment =	138,980

*£15,000 + £1,500

**£14,400 + £5,120

Trade and other receivables	£000
Trade and other receivables	17,234
Irrecoverable debts	–12
Trade and other receivables =	17,222

Trade and other payables	£000
Trade and other payables	9,854
Accruals – trial balance	256
Additional costs accrued	*35
Trade and other payables =	10,145

*distribution costs accrued

Retained earnings	£000
Retained earnings at start of year	9,280
Profit for year	4,458
Dividends paid	–2,000
Retained earnings =	11,738

Revaluation surplus	£000
Revaluation surplus at start of year	20,000
Other comprehensive income for year	9,500
Revaluation surplus =	29,500

Task 3

> **Matter 1**
> The new machine is recognised as an asset in the statement of financial position because:
> - it meets the definition of an asset – a resource controlled by the entity as a result of past events and from which future economic benefits are expected to flow
> - it satisfies the recognition criteria – it is probable that future economic benefits will flow to Foss Ltd and the machine has a cost or value that can be measured reliably
>
> Two measurement bases are:
> - historical cost, being the amount paid, or the fair value at the time of acquisition
> - realisable (settlement) value, being the amount that the asset could be sold for today
>
> **Matter 2**
> The relevant fundamental principle is confidentiality. An accountant must maintain the confidentiality of information, unless the information is a matter of public knowledge, or the accountant has the client's authority to disclose information. The requirement to maintain confidentiality includes when the accountant is in a social environment.

Task 4

> **(1)**   In accordance with IAS 36, *Impairment of Assets*, an impairment loss of £50,000 should be recognised as an expense in the company's statement of profit or loss, and £100,000 should be recognised as a decrease in other comprehensive income. This latter amount should be debited to the previously created revaluation surplus, ie the extent of the revaluation surplus for this asset. The carrying amount of the land should be reduced by £150,000 to £450,000.
>
> **(2)**   In accordance with IAS 37, *Provisions, Contingent Liabilities and Contingent Assets*, a provision of £100,000 should be recognised as an expense in the statement of profit or loss and a liability in the statement of financial position because:
>
> - Plant Ltd has a present obligation as a result of a past event
>
> - it is probable that an outflow of economic benefits will be required to settle the obligation
>
> - a reliable estimate can be made of the amount of the obligation
>
> Note that IAS 37 uses the word 'probable' to mean more likely than not to occur, ie a more than 50% likelihood of occurrence.

Task 5

(a)   False

(b)   (b)   At the lower of cost and net realisable value

(c)   (a)   1 only

(d)   (d)   All of them

(e)   (b)   £29,000

Task 6(a)   **Bravo Plc – Consolidated statement of financial position as at 31 March 20-1**

	£000
ASSETS	
Non-current assets	
Goodwill	490
Property, plant and equipment	3,670
	4,160
Current assets	1,740
Inventories	
Trade receivables	
Cash and cash equivalents	
	1,740
Total assets	5,900
EQUITY AND LIABILITIES	
Equity	
Share capital	2,000
Share premium	
Retained earnings	2,020
Non-controlling interest	410
Total equity	4,430
Non-current liabilities	570
Current liabilities	900
Total liabilities	1,470
Total equity and liabilities	5,900

Workings:

Goodwill	£000
Consideration	1,600
NCI at acquisition	370
Net assets acquired	−1,480
Goodwill =	490

Non-controlling interest (NCI)	£000
Share capital – attributable to NCI	250
Retained earnings – attributable to NCI	160
Non-controlling interest =	410

Retained earnings	£000
Parent	1,900
Subsidiary – attributable to parent	120
Retained earnings =	2,020

Inter-company transaction

£50,000 deducted from the current assets of Bravo Plc and from the current liabilities of Salvo Ltd

(b)   **Weiss Plc – Consolidated statement of profit or loss for the year ended 31 March 20-1**

	£000
Continuing operations	
Revenue	40,600
Cost of sales	–23,830
Gross profit	16,770
Other income	200
Distribution costs	–4,000
Administrative expenses	–2,300
Profit from operations	10,670
Finance costs	0
Profit before tax	10,670

Workings:

Revenue	£000
Parent	30,400
Subsidiary	10,300
Total inter-company adjustment	–100
Revenue =	40,600

Cost of sales	£000
Parent	17,800
Subsidiary	6,100
Total inter-company adjustment*	–70
Cost of sales =	23,830

*purchases –£100, unrealised profit £30[+] = cost of sales –£70

[+] unrealised profit is deducted from closing inventories; the effect of this is to increase cost of sales (because closing inventories are deducted in the cost of sales calculation)

Distribution costs
£3,000,000 + £1,000,000 = £4,000,000

Administrative expenses
£1,500,000 + £800,000 = £2,300,000

Profit before tax
£8,800,000 + £2,400,000 – £500,000 inter-company dividend – £30,000 unrealised profit
= £10,670,000

Task 7

Ratio	(a) Formula	(b) Calculation of ratio for Nelson Ltd
(1) Return on shareholders' funds	$\dfrac{\text{Profit after tax}}{\text{Total equity}} \times 100$	$\dfrac{1,764}{50,400} \times 100 \quad = \quad 3.5\%$
(2) Current ratio	$\dfrac{\text{Current assets}}{\text{Current liabilities}}$	$\dfrac{4,631}{2,105} \quad\quad = \quad 2.2{:}1$
(3) Asset turnover (net assets)	$\dfrac{\text{Revenue}}{\text{Total assets} - \text{current liabilities}}$	$\dfrac{32,400}{54,000 - 2,105} \quad = 0.6 \text{ times}$
(4) Gearing	$\dfrac{\text{Non-current liabilities}}{\substack{\text{Non-current liabilities} + \\ \text{total equity}}} \times 100$	$\dfrac{1,495}{1,495 + 50,400} \quad = \quad 2.9\%$
(5) Interest cover	$\dfrac{\text{Profit from operations}}{\text{Finance costs}}$	$\dfrac{2,754}{459} \quad\quad = 6.0 \text{ times}$

Task 8

(a)

REPORT

To: Steve Horan
From: AAT student
Subject: Shareholding in Blenheim Ltd
Date: Today

As requested I have looked into the financial situation of Blenheim Ltd.

(1) The **gross profit percentage** has deteriorated.

Less gross profit is being generated by sales/gross profit margin on sales.

Deterioration may be due to decreasing its sales price or increasing the cost of sales or both.

Could have been a change in the product mix.

(2) The **operating profit percentage** has improved.

More operating profit is being generated from sales – possibly an increase in sales volume.

Either an increase in the sales margins or a decrease in expenses, or both.

As the gross margins have deteriorated, must be the result of a decrease in expenses.

(3) The **inventory holding period** has deteriorated.

It now takes 18 days more to sell the inventory, on average, than it took the year before. This results in increased holding costs and possible inventory deterioration.

The increase might be due to slow moving inventory that might indicate possible obsolescence problems.

(4) The **trade receivables collection period** has deteriorated.

It now takes 15 days more to collect the debts, on average, than it took the year before.

It might be due to old debts which might become irrecoverable debts in the future.

(5) The **trade payables payment period** has deteriorated.

It now takes 8 days more to pay credit suppliers, on average, than it took the year before. This may be as a result of the longer time being taken to collect debts from customers.

If trade payables are not paid on time they could refuse to supply further goods to the company.

(b)

Steve should be advised to consider selling his shares since only the operating profit percentage has improved. The use of resources needs to be urgently reviewed by management as the periods for inventory, trade receivables and trade payables have all deteriorated.

Before making a final decision he should seek further financial information from the company.

Answers to practice assessment 2

Task 1 (a)   Kneale Ltd

Reconciliation of profit before tax to net cash from operating activities

	£000
Profit before tax	1,087
Adjustments for:	
Depreciation	727
Profit on disposal of PPE	−112
Finance costs	693
Adjustment in respect of inventories	251
Adjustment in respect of trade receivables	−309
Adjustment in respect of trade payable	918
Cash generated by operations	3,255
Tax paid	−491
Interest paid	−693
Net cash from operating activities	2,071

(b)   Kneale Ltd

Statement of cash flows for the year ended 31 March 20-1

	£000
Net cash from operating activities	2,071
Investing activities	
Proceeds on disposal of PPE	185
Purchases of PPE	−2,085
Net cash used in investing activities	−1,900
Financing activities	
Bank loans repaid	−1,750
Proceeds of share issue	1,200
Dividends paid	−350
Net cash used in financing activities	−900
Net increase/decrease in cash and cash equivalents	−729
Cash and cash equivalents at beginning of year	312
Cash and cash equivalents at end of year	−417

Workings:

Proceeds on disposal of property, plant and equipment	£000
Carrying amount of PPE sold	73
Profit on disposal of PPE	112
Total disposal proceeds =	185

Purchases of property, plant and equipment	£000
PPE at start of year	6,325
Depreciation charge	−727
Carrying amount of PPE sold	−73
PPE at end of year	−7,610
Total property, plant and equipment additions =	−2,085

Task 2

Kneale Ltd – Statement of changes in equity for the year ended 31 March 20-1

	Share capital £000	Share premium £000	Revaluation surplus £000	Retained earnings £000	Total equity £000
Balance at 1 April 20-0	1,500	210	0	6,043	7,753
Changes in equity					
Profit for the year				873	873
Dividends				−350	−350
Issue of share capital	1,000	200			1,200
Balance at 31 March 20-1	2,500	410	0	6,566	9,476

Task 3

Matter 1

The trade payable is recognised as a liability in the statement of financial position because:

- it meets the definition of a liability – a present obligation of Brayford Ltd arising from past events, the settlement of which is expected to result in an outflow of resources

- it satisfies the recognition criteria – it is probable that future economic benefits will flow from the entity and it has a cost or value that can be measured reliably   .

Two measurement bases are:

- historical cost, being the amount expected to be paid to the trade payable

- realisable (settlement) value, being the amount required to settle the liabilities today

Matter 2

The relevant fundamental principle is integrity. An accountant must not be associated with reports, returns, communications, or other information that:

- contains false or misleading statements

- contains statements or information furnished recklessly

- omits or obscures information so as to be misleading

Task 4

---

(1)   In accordance with IAS 38, *Intangible Assets*, the costs of development by Print Ltd could be an intangible asset, defined as an identifiable non-monetary asset without physical substance.

   However, before an intangible asset arising from development is recognised as an intangible asset in Print Ltd's financial statements, the company will have to demonstrate:

- the technical feasibility of completing the intangible asset so that it will be available for use or sale

- the intention to complete the intangible asset and to use or sell it

- its ability to use or sell the intangible asset

- the way in which the intangible asset will generate probable future economic benefits

- the availability of resources to complete the development and to use or sell the intangible asset

- its ability to measure reliably the expenditure attributable to the intangible asset

(2)   In accordance with IAS 10, *Events after the Reporting Period*, the amount of the debt is likely to be classed as an adjusting event.

   The bankruptcy of a major customer after the end of the financial year provides evidence of conditions that existed at the end of the reporting period. This is an adjusting event under IAS 10 and, if material, adjustments should be made to the amounts shown in the financial statements. Any such changes can only be made in the period:

- after the end of the financial year, and

- before the financial statements are authorised for issue (usually by the company's board of directors).

Task 5

(a)   True

(b)   (b)   £7,800

(c)   (c)   At the lower of the fair value of the asset being leased and the present value of the minimum lease payments

(d)   (c)   £20,400

(e)   (a)   Income arising in the course of an entity's ordinary activities

Task 6

(a)   **Severn Plc – Consolidated statement of financial position as at 31 March 20-1**

	£000
ASSETS	
Non-current assets	
Goodwill	130
Property, plant and equipment	2,800
	2,930
Current assets	1,100
	1,100
Total assets	4,030
EQUITY AND LIABILITIES	
Equity	
Share capital	2,000
Retained earnings	686
Non-controlling interest	404
Total equity	3,090
Non-current liabilities	320
Current liabilities	620
Total liabilities	940
Total equity and liabilities	4,030

Workings:

Goodwill	£000
Consideration	700
NCI at acquisition	380
Net assets acquired	–950
Goodwill =	130

Non-controlling interest (NCI)	£000
Share capital – attributable to NCI	280
Retained earnings – attributable to NCI	124
Non-controlling interest =	404

Retained earnings	£000
Parent	650
Subsidiary – attributable to parent	36
Retained earnings =	686

(b)   **Sinton Plc – Consolidated statement of profit or loss for the year ended 31 March 20-1**

	£000
Continuing operations	
Revenue	65,520
Cost of sales	–40,940
Gross profit	24,580
Other income	100
Distribution costs	–11,200
Administrative expenses	–5,200
Profit from operations	8,280
Finance costs	0
Profit before tax	8,280

Workings:

Revenue	£000
Parent	48,400
Subsidiary	17,200
Total inter-company adjustment*	−80
Revenue =	65,520

Cost of sale	£000
Parent	31,200
Subsidiary	9,800
Total inter-company adjustment*	−60
Cost of sales =	40,940

*purchases −£80, unrealised profit £20$^+$ = cost of sales −£60

$^+$unrealised profit is deducted from closing inventories; the effect of this is to increase cost of sales (because closing inventories are deducted in the cost of sales calculation)

Distribution costs

£8,000,000 + £3,200,000 = £11,200,000

Administrative expenses

£4,200,000 + £1,000,000 = £5,200,000

Profit before tax

£5,600,000 + £3,200,000 − £500,000 inter-company dividend − £20,000 unrealised profit = £8,280,000

Task 7

Ratio	(a) Formula	(b) Calculation of ratio for Laceby Ltd
(1) Gross profit percentage	$\dfrac{\text{Gross profit}}{\text{Revenue}} \times 100$	$\dfrac{22,680}{45,300} \times 100 \quad = \quad 50.1\%$
(2) Acid test (quick) ratio	$\dfrac{\text{Current assets} - \text{inventories}}{\text{Current liabilities}}$	$\dfrac{8,022 - 2,514}{3,338} \quad = \quad 1.7:1$
(3) Asset turnover (non-current assets)	$\dfrac{\text{Revenue}}{\text{Non-current assets}}$	$\dfrac{45,300}{77,094} \quad = 0.6 \text{ times}$
(4) Inventory holding period (days)	$\dfrac{\text{Inventories}}{\text{Cost of sales}} \times 365 \text{ days}$	$\dfrac{2,514}{22,620} \times 365 = 40.6 \text{ days}$
(5) Trade payables payment period	$\dfrac{\text{Trade payables}}{\text{Cost of sales}} \times 365 \text{ days}$	$\dfrac{2,715}{22,620} \times 365 = 43.8 \text{ days}$

Task 8

(a)

REPORT

To: Louise Forsythe
From: AAT student
Subject: Shareholding in Kingham Ltd
Date: Today

As requested I have looked into the financial situation of Kingham Ltd.

(1) **Gross profit percentage** has deteriorated.

Less gross profit is being generated by sales/gross profit margin on sales.

Deterioration may be due to decreasing its sales price or increasing the cost of sales or both.

Could have been a change in the product mix.

(2) **Operating profit percentage** has improved.

More operating profit is being generated from sales – possibly an increase in sales volume.

Either an increase in the sales margins or a decrease in expenses, or both.

As the gross margins have deteriorated, must be the result of a decrease in expenses.

(3) **Return on shareholders' funds** has improved.

More profit after tax is being generated from shareholders' funds.

The equity of the company is being utilised more efficiently and is providing a better return on the shareholders' investment than in previous years.

(4) **Gearing** has improved.

The company may have repaid loans during the year, or equity has increased from higher retained earnings as a result of a profitable company.

This makes it less risky.

Interest payments will be reduced.

Gives the company the ability to borrow in the future should it need to do so.

(5) **Interest cover** has improved.

More operating profit to cover interest payments.

This makes the company less risky.

Caused by higher operating profits/lower interest payments.

Lower interest payments could be due to loans being repaid (lower gearing) during the year.

(b)

Louise should be advised to consider maintaining her shares since, while gross profit percentage has deteriorated, operating profit percentage and return on shareholders' funds have both improved. The company is in a better financial position with reduced gearing and higher interest cover – both of these make the company less risky.

Before making a final decision she should seek further financial information from the company.

Answers to practice assessment 3

Task 1

(a)   **Chen Ltd**

Reconciliation of profit before tax to net cash from operating activities

	£000
Profit before tax	9,562
Adjustments for:	
Depreciation	4,275
Dividends received	−84
Loss on disposal of PPE	40
Finance costs	212
Adjustment in respect of inventories	−1,672
Adjustment in respect of trade receivables	−309
Adjustment in respect of trade payables	−73
Cash generated by operations	11,951
Tax paid	−2,148
Interest paid	−212
Net cash from operating activities	9,591

(b)   **Chen Ltd**

Statement of cash flows for the year ended 31 March 20-1

	£000
Net cash from operating activities	9,591
Investing activities	
Dividends received	84
Proceeds on disposal of PPE	384
Purchases of PPE	−11,469
Net cash used in investing activities	−11,001
Financing activities	
Bank loans repaid	−1,750
Proceeds of share issue	3,000
Dividends paid	−554
Net cash from financing activities	696
Net increase/decrease in cash and cash equivalents	−714
Cash and cash equivalents at beginning of year	430
Cash and cash equivalents at end of year	−284

Workings:

Proceeds on disposal of property, plant and equipment	£000
Carrying amount of PPE sold	424
Loss on disposal of PPE	–40
Total disposal proceeds =	384

Purchases of property, plant and equipment	£000
PPE at start of year	32,860
Depreciation charge	–4,275
Carrying amount of PPE sold	–424
PPE at end of year	–39,630
Total property, plant and equipment additions =	–11,469

Task 2

Chen Ltd – Statement of changes in equity for the year ended 31 March 20-1

	Share capital £000	Share premium £000	Revaluation surplus £000	Retained earnings £000	Total equity £000
Balance at 1 April 20-0	10,000	4,000	0	21,749	35,749
Changes in equity					
Profit for the period				6,195	6,195
Dividends				–554	–554
Issue of share capital	2,000	1,000			3,000
Balance at 31 March 20-1	12,000	5,000	0	27,390	44,390

Task 3

> ### Matter 1
>
> The objective of general purpose financial reporting according to the IASB's *Conceptual Framework for Financial Reporting* is:
>
> > "to provide financial information about the reporting entity that is useful to existing and potential investors, lenders and other creditors in making decisions about providing resources to the entity."
>
> The users of financial statements identified in the Conceptual Framework are:
>
> - existing investors – whether to continue to hold, to sell, or to buy more shares in the company
> - potential investors – whether to buy shares in the company
> - lenders – whether to make a loan to the company
> - other creditors – whether to supply the company with goods and services
>
> ### Matter 2
>
> The relevant fundamental principle is objectivity. An accountant must not allow bias, conflict of interest or the undue influence of others to override professional or business judgements.

Task 4

> **(1)** In accordance with IAS 16, *Property, Plant and Equipment*, the depreciation charge for this item of machinery for the current year to 31 December 20-4 is £30,000.
>
> As there has been a change in the useful life from previous estimates it is necessary to calculate the carrying amount at the date of the change. This is £220,000 (£340,000 less three years' depreciation at £40,000 [£240,000 ÷ 6 years] per year). The remaining useful life is expected to be four years, with the residual value still expected to be £100,000. The revised depreciation calculation is (£220,000 – £100,000)/4 years = £30,000 per year.
>
> **(2)** In accordance with IAS 12, *Income Taxes*, Carpets Ltd will recognise the tax expense for the year (from ordinary activities) on the face of the statement of profit or loss and other comprehensive income. The amount of unpaid current tax is recognised as a liability on the statement of financial position.
>
> As Carpets Ltd over-estimated its corporation tax liability for the previous financial year by £4,000, its financial statements for 20-4 will adjust for this prior period and show:
>
> - statement of profit or loss and other comprehensive income:
>
>   corporation tax charge £26,000 (ie £30,000 estimated for 20-4, less £4,000 over-estimated in 20-3).
>
> - statement of financial position: corporation tax liability £30,000 (ie the estimated tax payable for 20-4).

Task 5

(a) False

(b) (d) All of them

(c) (d) 2 and 4

(d) (a) Identifiability, future economic benefits, control

(e) (a) £27,000

Task 6

Lee Plc – Consolidated statement of financial position as at 31 December 20-0

	£000
ASSETS	
Non-current assets	
Goodwill	940
Property, plant and equipment	6,365
	7,305
Current assets	3,187
Total assets	10,492
EQUITY AND LIABILITIES	
Equity	
Share capital	3,500
Share premium	750
Retained earnings	1,360
Non-controlling interest	810
Total equity	6,420
Non-current liabilities	405
Current liabilities	3,667
Total liabilities	4,072
Total equity and liabilities	10,492

Workings:

Goodwill	£000
Consideration	3,400
NCI at acquisition	780
Net assets acquired	–3,120
Impairment of goodwill	–120
Goodwill =	940

Non-controlling interest (NCI)	£000
Share capital – attributable to NCI	500
Share premium – attributable to NCI	125
Revaluation reserve – attributable to NCI	50
Retained earnings – attributable to NCI	135
Non-controlling interest =	810

Retained earnings	£000
Parent	1,390
Impairment	–120
Subsidiary – attributable to parent	90
Retained earnings =	1,360

Property, plant and equipment	£000
Consolidated PPE prior ro fair value adjustment	6,165
Adjustment to fair value	200
	6,365

Task 7

Ratio	(a) Formula	(b) Calculation of ratio for Dodia Ltd
(1) Operating profit percentage	$\dfrac{\text{Profit from operations}}{\text{Revenue}}$ x 100	$\dfrac{7,347}{64,300}$ x 100 = 11.4%
(2) Acid test (quick) ratio	$\dfrac{\text{Current assets} - \text{Inventories}}{\text{Current liabilities}}$	$\dfrac{9,338 - 3,695}{5,222}$ = 1.1:1
(3) Asset turnover (net assets) (times)	$\dfrac{\text{Revenue}}{\text{Total assets} - \text{Current liabilities}}$	$\dfrac{64,300}{38,138 - 5,222}$ = 2.0 times
(4) Trade payables payment period (days)	$\dfrac{\text{Trade payables}}{\text{Cost of sales}}$ x 365	$\dfrac{3,174}{39,163}$ x 365 = 29.6 days
(5) Interest cover (times)	$\dfrac{\text{Profit from operations}}{\text{Finance costs}}$	$\dfrac{7,347}{1,054}$ = 7.0 times

Task 8

email
To: joanna.fisher@faloye.co.uk
From: aatstudent@fstmexam
Subject: Analysis of working capital and suggestions for improvement
Date: 15 April 20-2

As requested I have analysed the working capital of Faloye Limited by means of comparing four accounting ratios for the company with those of industry averages. My analysis is as follows:

(a)

Current ratio is worse

- Faloye Ltd has fewer current assets available to meet its current liabilities than the industry average.
- Looks to be too low and is likely to give problems in meeting current liabilities as they fall due. Inventory holding period is longer than average and, taking into account the other ratios, it is likely that cash is low or overdrawn – which could be the reason for the longer trade payables payment period.

Inventory holding period is worse

- Faloye Ltd is selling inventories more slowly than the industry average.
- Could be due to old/obsolete inventories/less demand from customers/poor inventory management systems.

Trade receivables collection period is better

- Faloye Ltd is collecting its receivables slightly quicker than the industry average, indicating efficient credit control.
- Could be due to shorter credit terms being offered, which may lead customers to look to other suppliers with better terms.

Trade payables payment period is considerably longer – worse for supplier goodwill, but better for cash flow

- Faloye Ltd is paying trade payables slower than the industry average.
- While this is good for cash flow, it may lead to problems if suppliers press for payment.
- Not good for supplier goodwill.
- Faloye Ltd is unlikely to be able to take advantage of prompt payment discounts offered by suppliers.

(b)

Suggestions to improve management of working capital

- Increase turnover of inventory/reduce inventory levels, eg improve inventory control procedures, reduce selling prices (although this will have a negative impact on both profitability and cash).
- Further reduce trade receivable days, eg improve collection procedures, reduce credit periods, offer prompt payment discounts to encourage quicker settlement, albeit with a negative impact on cash.
- Formalise current terms with trade payables so as to avoid demands for immediate payment.

Appendix

These pages may be photocopied for student use.

It is recommended that they are enlarged to A4 size.

These pages are also available for download from the Products and Resources Section of www.osbornebooks.co.uk

The forms and formats are:

Statement of profit or loss and other comprehensive income for the year ended.........

	£000
Revenue	
Cost of sales	
Gross profit	
Distribution costs	
Administrative expenses	
Profit from operations	
Finance costs	
Profit before tax	
Tax	
Profit for the year from continuing operations	
Other comprehensive income for the year	
Total comprehensive income for the year	

Workings

Cost of sales	£000
Cost of sales =	

Select from the following list:

- Accruals
- Closing inventories
- Depreciation
- Opening inventories
- Prepayments
- Purchases

Distribution costs	£000
Distribution costs =	

Select from the following list:

- Accruals
- Irrecoverable debts
- Depreciation
- Distribution costs
- Prepayments

Administrative expenses	£000
Administrative expenses =	

Select from the following list:

- Accruals
- Administrative expenses
- Irrecoverable debts
- Depreciation
- Prepayments

- -

Tax	£000
Tax =	

Select from the following list:

- Current year
- Previous year

Statement of changes in equity for the year ended . . . .

	Share capital	Share premium	Revaluation surplus	Retained earnings	Total equity
	£000	*£000*	*£0000*	*£000*	*£000*
Balance at start of the year					
Changes in equity					
Total comprehensive income*					
Dividends					
Issue of share capital					
Balance at end of year					

*'Profit for the period', if no other comprehensive income

Statement of financial position as at . . . .

	£000
ASSETS	
Non-current assets	
Current assets	
Total assets	
EQUITY AND LIABILITIES	
Equity	
Total equity	
Non-current liabilities	
Current liabilities	
Total liabilities	
Total equity and liabilities	

Select from the following list:

- Bank loans
- Cash and cash equivalents
- Debenture loans
- Inventories
- Property, plant and equipment
- Retained earnings

- Revaluation surplus
- Share capital
- Share premium
- Tax liabilities
- Trade and other payables
- Trade and other receivables

Workings

Property, plant and equipment	£000
Property, plant and equipment =	

Select from the following list:

- Accrumulated dep'n – land and buildings
- Accrumulated dep'n – plant and equipment
- Land and buildings – value
- Plant and equipment – cost
- Revaluation – land and buildings

- -

Trade and other receivables	£000
Trade and other receivables =	

Select from the following list:

- Accruals – trial balance
- Additional costs/expenses prepaid
- Prepayments – trial balance
- Trade and other receivables
- Additional costs/expenses accrued
- Irrecoverable debts
- Trade and other payables

Trade and other payables	£000
Trade and other payables =	

Select from the following list:

- Accruals – trial balance
- Additional costs/expenses prepaid
- Prepayments – trial balance
- Trade and other payables

- Additional costs/expenses accrued
- Dividends
- Taxation liability
- Trade and other receivables

- -

Retained earnings	£000
Retained earnings =	

Select from the following list:

- Dividends paid
- Other comprehensive income for the year
- Retained earnings at start of the year
- Revaluation surplus
- Total comprehensive income for the year
- Total profit for the year

Revaluation surplus	*£000*
Revaluation surplus =	

Select from the following list:

- Dividends paid
- Other comprehensive income for the year
- Retained earnings at start of the year
- Revaluation surplus at start of the year
- Total comprehensive income for the year
- Total profit for the year

Reconciliation of profit before tax to net cash from operating activities

	£000
Adjustments for:	
Cash generated by operations	
Net cash from operations	

Select from the following list:

- Adjustment in respect of inventories
- Adjustment in respect of trade payables
- Adjustment in respect of trade receivables
- Bank loans
- Depreciation
- Dividends paid
- Dividends received
- Finance costs
- Profit/loss on disposal of PPE
- Interest paid

- New bank loans
- Proceeds on disposal of PPE
- Profit after tax
- Profit before tax
- Profit from operations
- Purchases of PPE
- Revaluation surplus
- Tax paid

Statement of cash flows for the year ended ....

	£000
Net cash from operations	
Investing activities	
Net cash used in/from investing activities	
Financing activities	
Net cash used in/from financing activities	
Net increase/decrease in cash and cash equivalents	
Cash and cash equivalents at beginning of year	
Cash and cash equivalents at end of year	

Select from the following list:

- Adjustment in respect of inventories
- Adjustment in respect of trade payables
- Adjustment in respect of trade receivables
- Bank loans
- Dividends paid
- Dividends received
- New bank loans
- Proceeds of share issue
- Proceeds on disposal of PPE
- Purchases of PPE
- Revaluation

Workings

Proceeds on disposal of property, plant and equipment	£000
Total disposal proceeds =	

Select from the following list:

- Carrying amount of PPE sold
- Depreciation charge
- Profit/loss on disposal of PPE
- PPE at end of year
- PPE at start of year
- Revaluation

Purchases of property, plant and equipment	£000
PPE at start of year	
Total property, plant and equipment additions =	

Select from the following list:

- Carrying amount of PPE sold
- Depreciation charge
- Profit/loss on disposal of PPE
- PPE at end of year
- Revaluation

Consolidated statement of profit or loss for the year ended . . . .

	£000
Continuing operations	
Revenue	
Cost of sales	
Gross profit	
Other income	
Distribution costs	
Administrative expenses	
Profit from operations	
Finance costs	
Profit before tax	
Tax	
Profit for the year from continuing operations	

Attributable to	£000
Equity holders of the parent	
Non-controlling interest	
Profit for the period from continuing operations =	

Workings

Revenue	£000
Parent	
Subsidiary	
Total inter-company adjustment*	
Revenue =	

*enter '0' if no adjustment needed

Cost of sales	£000
Parent	
Subsidiary	
Total inter-company adjustment*	
Cost of sales =	

*enter '0' if no adjustment needed

Consolidated statement of financial position as at . . . .

	£000
ASSETS	
Non-current assets	
Goodwill	
Property, plant and equipment	
Current assets	
Inventories	
Trade receivables	
Cash and cash equivalents	
Total assets	
EQUITY AND LIABILITIES	
Equity	
Share capital	
Share premium	
Retained earnings	
Non-controlling interest	
Total equity	
Non-current liabilities	
Current liabilities	
Trade payables	
Tax liabilities	
Total liabilities	
Total equity and liabilities	

Workings

Goodwill	£000
Goodwill =	

Select from the following list:

- Impairment of goodwill
- NCI at acquisition
- Consideration
- Net assets acquired

- -

Non-controlling interest (NCI)	£000
Non-controlling interest =	

Select from the following list:

- Current assets – attributable to NCI
- Non-current assets – attributable to NCI
- Retained earnings – attributable to NCI
- Share capital – attributable to NCI
- Impairment of goodwill
- Price paid
- Revaluation surplus – attributable to NCI
- Share premium – attributable to NCI

Retained earnings	£000
Retained earnings =	

Select from the following list:

- Impairment of goodwill
- Inter-company adjustment
- Parent
- Revaluation
- Subsidiary – attributable to parent

Property, plant and equipment	£000

Select from the following list:

- Adjustment to fair value
- Consolidated PPE prior to fair value adjustment

for your notes

for your notes

for your notes

for your notes

for your notes

for your notes

for your notes

for your notes

for your notes

for your notes

for your notes

for your notes